LORD LISTER

LORD LISTER, 1827–1912

LORD LISTER

His Life and Doctrine

by

DOUGLAS GUTHRIE *1885—*

Success depends upon attention to detail—LISTER

BALTIMORE

THE WILLIAMS AND WILKINS COMPANY

1949

TO
ALL DOCTORS' WIVES
AND ESPECIALLY TO
ONE OF THEM

Made in Great Britain

PREFACE

EIGHTY-FOUR years have passed since Joseph Lister made the discovery which was destined to revolutionise surgery. Great advances have been made during that period, and methods and techniques have altered to such an extent that some of Lister's teaching has become obsolete, although the principles which he laid down remain inviolate.

Accordingly, to the present generation Lister has become almost a legend, and the value of his contribution is not always fully appreciated. For this reason an attempt has been made, in the following pages, to view the achievement of Lister in the light of modern knowledge, and to add to the familiar facts of his life story some further data which recently have become available. Each fresh detail of the life and work of the greatest surgeon of history must surely be of interest and of value.

No one can contribute to the growing collection of Listeriana without referring to the admirable biography of Lord Lister by his nephew Sir Rickman Godlee, published in 1914, and the present writer is grateful to Messrs. Macmillan & Co. for permission to draw upon that work for certain facts relating to Lister's parentage and early life. This information has been supplemented from other sources rendered available by Mr. J. Lister Harrison, Sir John Parsons, Professor Rudolf Matas, Professor Grey Turner, Professor Walter Mercer, Mr. J. M. Graham, Mr. J. N. Jackson Hartley, and others.

The writer acknowledges especially his indebtedness to the University of Edinburgh and the Royal College of Surgeons of England for their kind permission to publish for the first time certain autograph letters in their possession. He is most grateful to his friend and former teacher Mr. W. J. Stuart, who read the original manuscript and who made many helpful suggestions. He also thanks the publishers for their unfailing courtesy and patience during the preparation of this work.

D. G.

21 CLARENDON CRESCENT,
    EDINBURGH.
    October 1949.

CONTENTS

LIST OF PLATES

CHAPTER I

SURGERY BEFORE LISTER

IF the magnitude of a man's achievement is to be judged by the number of human lives he has saved, Joseph Lister must surely be regarded as one of the leading benefactors of humanity. His is a name which should receive the reverence and homage of all mankind.

Not only did he raise surgery from the status of a craft to that of a science, he introduced into it a principle which has preserved the lives of countless thousands.

Indeed, his work was so revolutionary that the entire history of surgery falls very naturally into two epochs: before Lister, and after Lister; two very different pictures, presenting a contrast almost unbelievable. The present generation is apt to take for granted the vast changes which Lister wrought. Attempts have even been made to belittle his remarkable work or to attribute the credit to others. Less than a century has passed since the date of his discovery, and the improvement initiated by his methods remains a wonder to every thinking student of surgery. Who, indeed, could fail to be impressed by the results of modern surgery?

To-day, the surgeon carries on his work with confidence, knowing very well that within a week or ten days, when he comes to remove the stitches, he will find the wound healed, leaving a scar so slight that, a few months later, it may be scarcely visible. Thousands of operations, now performed daily, leave wounds which heal in this fashion, with great benefit to the patient and with a minimum of risk.

All this we owe to Lister, the man who made surgery safe. What a contrast there is between this picture and that of the pre-Listerian epoch.

Before Lister's day, a wound was so liable to cause serious trouble that the surgeon hesitated to inflict it. A surgical operation might be technically perfect, yet no one could predict the result. Although, some twenty years prior to Lister's discovery, the discovery of anæsthesia had abolished the dreadful pain caused by the surgeon's knife, the risk remained as great as ever.

The horrors of an operation in the pre-anæsthetic days have often been described. Charles Darwin, who entered upon the study of medicine, but never completed the course, recounts in his autobiography how, to use his own words, he "attended on two occasions the operating-theatre in the hospital at Edinburgh, and saw two very bad operations, one on a child, but I rushed away before they were completed. Nor did I ever attend again, for hardly any inducement would have been strong enough to make me do so; this being long before the blessed days of chloroform. The two cases fairly haunted me for many a long year." That was in 1826.

A few years later, about 1830, James Young Simpson, who was to gain immortal fame as the discoverer of chloroform anæsthesia, was "so sickened at the suffering he witnessed in the operating-theatre, very early in his student days, that he had shrunk from the scene, decided to abandon his medical studies and seek his way in the paths of law." But he turned slowly again from the Parliament House, with its "interminable pattering of legal feet," back to the Infirmary, for he knew it was cowardly to desert the colours under which he had enrolled. Like the true soldier he was, he determined to use such powers as had been granted him to fight a good fight more especially against "that foretaste and small change of death—pain."

In the more modern words of Lord Moynihan, "the responsibility of the surgeon is a very heavy one; indeed, there is none so heavy . . . he must prove himself worthy of it or choose other work." In pre-anæsthetic days the strain and trial of a surgical operation bore heavily upon the operator and even upon the onlooker. From the patient's point of view, the agony of the procedure was almost past imagining. The following description of an eye-witness of the early days of surgery in America conveys some idea of the feelings of the unhappy patient:—

"She is cheered by kind words, and the information that it will soon be over. . . . She is enjoined to be calm and to keep quiet and still. But of what avail are all her attempts at fortitude! At the first clear crisp cut of the scalpel, agonising screams burst from her, and with convulsive struggles she endeavours to leap from the table. But the force is nigh. Strong men throw themselves upon her and pinion her limbs. Shrieks upon shrieks make their horrible way into the stillness of the room until the heart of the boldest sinks in his bosom like a lump of lead. At length it is finished, and, prostrated with pain, weak from her exertions and bruised by the violence used, she is borne from the amphitheatre to her bed in the ward to recover from exhaustion."

Small wonder indeed that even to-day our patients are terrified by the tradition that clings to the word "operation," which was indeed so terrible a procedure in the early days.

2

It is true that before Lister came on the scene, the actual operation had been robbed of much of its ordeal of terror, but after its performance many dangers lay ahead. The poor patient was still obliged to face the risk of complications which caused intense suffering, long illness and, often, death. A few days after the operation the wound would become inflamed and aching, as the dreaded blood-poisoning appeared and assumed one or other of its terrible forms. Such a sequence of events was extremely common; so frequent, indeed, that the rapid and painless healing of a wound such as every surgeon now expects, healing "by first intention," as it was called, was regarded then as an extraordinary occurrence.

The contrast between the two periods, before and after Lister, may be emphasised still further by two quotations descriptive of the healing of wounds, the first written a year before Lister's discovery, the second a few years ago. When Lister was commencing his researches, James Spence, Professor of Surgery in Edinburgh, was writing a text-book (1864) in which he made the following statement regarding wounds:—

"The edges may adhere and become incorporated, but this is rare, except in the most trifling incisions."

How very different is the account given in the recent work (1938) by Professor Illingworth, the present occupant of Lister's Chair at Glasgow. He states:—

"If the margins of a clean incised wound are accurately co-apted, healing takes place with little disturbance."

GENIUS AND DISCOVERY

It must not be imagined, however, that the discovery which led to so complete and revolutionary a change of surgical outlook was a sudden and unheralded event. Previous workers had opened the new fields of knowledge which made Lister's achievement possible, and he constantly acknowledged his debt to his predecessors. Yet he possessed the genius which they lacked; he found something which had eluded the quest of previous seekers after knowledge.

The march of human progress is not a steady advance. There are hills and valleys, dark ages and times of revival, failures and successes. New ideas and methods appear. Some are preserved, others are discarded. At times so many new paths are followed that the traveller becomes quite bewildered. Then there appears the genius who shows us that all those

3

ways, apparently diverging, are really leading towards the same destination.

Before the time of Isaac Newton, the nature of the physical universe was a subject of research among natural philosophers, who held what seemed to be the most diverse views. Newton united all their vague speculations by enunciating a set of laws, which simplified everything.

William Harvey, too, had many heralds. More than one of them came very near to the discovery of the circulation of the blood. For example, Fabricius, Harvey's teacher at Padua, described the valves of the veins, the "little doors," as he called them, which allowed only a one-way traffic. Nevertheless none but a genius like Harvey, in beholding those valves, could have argued: "Then where does all the blood go? Where does it all come from?" In no brain but his had there dawned the idea that "there might be a movement, as it were, in a circle."

So also was it with Lister. Standing on the shoulders of his predecessors, he beheld something that was invisible to them. The precursors of Lister lacked his insight, although they supplied him with the materials essential for his quest.

History is the basis of all human progress. Unless we know what has already been done, we shall simply repeat and perpetuate the mistakes of our ancestors, and add nothing to the sum of human achievement.

Accordingly, the logical method of approach to any study of the life and work of Lister is to commence by glancing backward at the past. In order to appreciate the significance of his contribution to human well-being, it is necessary in the first place to have some knowledge of the rise and progress of surgery during the preceding centuries, and, in particular, to ascertain what were the views held by the earlier surgeons in regard to the healing of wounds. In the second place, it is essential to the understanding of Lister's achievement that the reader should know something of the evolution of the idea of the infection of wounds by living microorganisms.

THE EVOLUTION OF WOUND TREATMENT

The art of surgery is probably much older than the art of medicine. Injury demanded more energetic and immediate attention than did disease. Disease, indeed, was regarded by prehistoric man as a magical, and not as a natural, phenomenon. A similar belief was held by primitive races in more recent times, nor is it altogether unknown at the present day. Disease, according to primitive thought, was an affliction sent by the gods as a punishment, or projected at the victim by a malevolent spirit or

4

even by a human enemy. Consequently the treatment consisted in casting out the evil influence by rites and incantations, or by invoking the assistance of a sorcerer or medicine man, or a physician of the priestly class.

Surgery, however, must have arisen in a fashion altogether different. No such mystery surrounded its beginnings. The wounds or fractures or other injuries to which primitive man was liable, whether in hunting or in combat, were too real and obvious to be regarded from such an angle. Just as a wounded animal licks the wound, so did man apply his greater intelligence in binding it up, in arresting bleeding by pressure, and in applying splints to support fractured limbs. All this must have been done at a very early stage in man's history, probably long before he learned to employ the juices of plants as medicines or as poisons. The leaf of a tree or shrub was doubtless the first dressing ever used.

Naturally, too, the treatment of bodily injuries was practised long before any attempt was made to perform any surgical operation for the relief of disease. Antiseptics may well have been the first medicaments in history, although, of course, the name is of relatively modern date, as we shall have occasion to note in a later chapter. The fact essential to the present argument is, that although many centuries have elapsed since antiseptic applications were first applied in the treatment of wounds, they were applied in an altogether random and haphazard fashion before Lister showed the reason for their use.

The art and science of medicine, like so many other branches of human knowledge, came to us from the East. Although the title is occasionally contested by those who espouse the claims of Shen Nung, an early Chinese philosopher, or those of Imhotep, the Egyptian vizier and pyramid builder, both of whom lived about 2900 B.C., the pride of place as the "Father of Medicine" is usually accorded, individually, to Hippocrates and, collectively, to the Hippocratic school which he founded. Born in the little island of Cos, in the Aegean Sea, about 460 B.C., Hippocrates is said to have been the first to separate medicine from magic, and to confer upon it the high ethical status which it has since maintained.

He did not confine his practice to medicine. He was also a good surgeon, treating fractures by the use of splints, reducing dislocated joints, and even trephining the skull, as he so clearly describes in the work *On Wounds in the Head*. Of peculiar interest to the present discussion is the fact that he employed wine and tar in the dressing of wounds. Wine, indeed, is a very ancient antiseptic, and it will be recollected that the Good Samaritan treated the wounds of his patient by "pouring in oil and wine."

After the Græco-Roman period, medicine and surgery passed into the

5

hands of the Arabs. In the vast Moslem Empire, which extended as far as Spain, there were many surgeons, although this empire arose during the period of the Dark Ages, when the level of learning sank low and little original work was accomplished. The Arab surgeons disliked the use of the knife, and preferred red-hot irons or cauteries, a practice which persisted until the Renaissance.

By that time, medical learning had come to Europe by way of the famous School of Salerno, anatomy had received careful study at Padua and elsewhere, and the time was ripe for a revival of surgery.

THE HUMANITY OF AMBROISE PARÉ

The greatest surgeon of the Renaissance was Ambroise Paré. Like many another surgeon, he had gained his experience in military service. Thirty years with the armies of France had taught him much, and the story he tells in his *Journeys in Divers Places* is a thrilling and vivid picture of those times. Gunpowder had recently been introduced, and Paré, in 1537, was called upon to treat wounds much more terrible than those produced by darts or arrows. Paré writes:—

> "Now at that time I was a fresh-water soldier, I had not seen wounds made by gunshot. It is true that I had read in John de Vigo that he commands to treat wounds made by weapons of fire by cauterising them with oil of elders scalding hot."

At length the supply of oil ran short, and Paré "was constrained instead thereof to apply the digestive of yolks of Eggs, Oil of Roses, and Turpentine," and to his surprise this produced far better results than cauterising. "Then I resolved with my self," he concludes, "never so cruelly to burn poor men wounded with gunshot."

Ambroise Paré recognised the healing power of Nature, that principle so strongly stated by Hippocrates, and he never tired of repeating his oft-quoted remark, "I dressed him, but God healed him." Nevertheless he appears to have given most of the credit to the applications of the surgeon, as one may infer from his lengthy lists of the drugs he was wont to apply: aloes, styrax, pix, bugloss, lily-root, horsetail and many others classified into such strange categories as deterzives, epulolicks, pyrotics, agglutinatives, and so on.

Richard Wiseman, who was Surgeon to the Royal Forces during the Civil War, states in his *Several Chirurgicall Treatises*, of 1676, that he treated wounds with "pledgits spread with a mixture of turpentine and yolk of egg."

A favourite dressing of more ancient date was Friar's Balsam, still in use as tincture of benzoin.

Doubtless many of those substances were good antiseptics, but the idea underlying their use was that the surgeon was forcing the wound to heal by the application of "carnefying" dressings, and not merely assisting the work of Nature. This was a fallacy which persisted right up to the time of Lister, who repeatedly used to tell his students, "There is no such thing as a 'healing' ointment."

LAUDABLE PUS

Another persistent fallacy, and one which had a very direct bearing upon the work of Lister, was the belief that suppuration was a normal stage in the healing of a wound. It was an idea which probably dated from the time of Galen (A.D. 200). Paré himself praised the value of "suppurating medicines" applied to wounds. "A suppurating medicine," wrote Paré, "is said to be that which, shutting the pores and preventing transferation by his emplastic consistence, increaseth the matter and native heat and turneth the matter cast out of the vessels into pus and sauces." The error was perpetuated until eventually the product of suppuration, the pus or matter, which so regularly appeared, became a thing to be favoured, and received the name of "laudable pus."

Even in 1748 we find John Freke, Surgeon to St. Bartholomew's Hospital, writing a book with the long title *An Essay on the Art of Healing, in which Pus Laudabile or Matter, as also Incarning and Cicatrising, and the Causes of various Diseases, are endeavoured to be accounted for both from Nature and Reason.* Laudable pus, extolled as essential even until the eighteenth century, became gradually recognised as an evil, but the majority of surgeons actually regarded it as a necessary evil. It was Lister who clearly and conclusively proved how unnecessary it was.

Long before pus was lauded in this manner, the process of healing by suppuration was thought to be the normal sequence of events. The error probably arose during the Middle Ages, but even then there were a few enlightened surgeons, such as Theodoric of Bologna, in the thirteenth century, who opposed it strongly, stating that the formation of pus in wounds was unnecessary and undesirable.

Still more advanced was the teaching of Paracelsus, that most violent and revolutionary reformer of the Renaissance period who publicly burned the books of his predecessors as an expression of his contempt for them, and who, naturally enough, was not popular with his contemporaries. Nevertheless there is much wisdom in the voluminous writings

7

of Paracelsus, and he was never wiser than when he alluded to "Nature, the physician of wounds." Nature healed wounds by sealing the edges with a "balsam" manufactured by the body. The passage is worth quoting:—

> "Warily must the surgeon take heed not to remove or interfere with Nature's balsam which healeth wounds. Nature has her own doctor in every limb; wherefore every surgeon should know that it is not he, but Nature, who heals."

Such an opinion would have been fully approved by Lister. Lister, however, went much further than his predecessors, when he showed *how* Nature could be assisted, and *why* antiseptics were useful in dressing wounds. Even Lister made no progress until he had discovered the reason for the frequent failure of Nature's best efforts, and the actual cause of inflammation and suppuration in wounds.

Consequently, as a further preface to the study of what Lister accomplished, we must glance in another direction; this time at some of the older views regarding the transmission of disease, views which culminated in the discovery of those "germs" which were proved by Lister to be the cause of wound infection, the chief barrier to the successful practice of surgery.

"Germs" revealed by the Microscope

The idea that disease might be caused by tiny particles in the air was one which had been envisaged since ancient times. Even as early as the tenth century there are references in Saxon manuscripts to flying venom or "elf shot."

Knowledge of such "air-borne" disease remained very vague until it was carried a stage further by the Veronese nobleman, Fracastorius, who was a student at Padua along with his friend Copernicus, early in the sixteenth century. Copernicus was drawn to astronomy, while Fracastorius became keenly interested in epidemic disease.

Although a century was to pass before the invention of the microscope placed in men's hands a means of studying the tiny microbes and disease germs which are now such familiar objects, Fracastorius presumed that they existed. He suggested that many diseases might be caused by imperceptible particles or "seminaria, the seeds of disease which multiply rapidly and propagate their like." In his great work, *De Contagione*, which he published in 1546, he describes three modes of infection: infection by contact, infection by clothing, utensils, etc., which he called "fomites,"

8

and infection at a distance, by the air. Subsequent discoveries have proved the truth of his theory, and he well deserves his title as the pioneer of epidemiology.

The microscope, when first employed in medicine at about this time, was far from perfect. Many improvements and modifications were necessary before an instrument was constructed sufficiently powerful to reveal the minute micro-organisms of disease. Even Lister was at first unable to demonstrate the germs, of which he spoke so confidently, although his father was one of those who improved the optical qualities of the microscope as it then existed.

The early history of the microscope is obscure. It is certain that magnifying lenses were used in ancient times, and the credit of combining lenses in a tube, to form the compound microscope, is usually accorded to a Dutch spectacle-maker, Zacharias Jansen. This was in 1609. Although Athanasius Kircher of Wurzburg claimed to have found in the blood of plague-stricken patients "countless masses of small worms, invisible to the naked eye," it is generally believed that what Kircher saw were blood corpuscles and not plague bacilli. Indeed, the microscope was not accepted seriously for many years, and was regarded simply as a toy.

One of the greatest and certainly one of the most industrious pioneers of microscopy was Antony van Leeuwenhoek (1632-1723), the Dutch linen-draper who devoted his long life of ninety-one years to grinding his own lenses, making his own microscopes, hundreds of them, and describing the wonders they revealed. The film from his own teeth, for instance, was found to contain "little animals, more numerous than all the people in the Netherlands." With his simple microscope Leeuwenhoek made many discoveries, which he communicated to the Royal Society, of which he became a Fellow, although he never visited London.

In England, too, were devotees of the microscope: Robert Hooke, one of the founders of the Royal Society, who wrote his beautifully illustrated *Micrographia* in 1665; Nehemiah Grew, who revealed many microscopic wonders of plant life, and many others.

Spontaneous Generation

About this time there arose much argument regarding the theory of "spontaneous generation," as it was called. Were mites generated from cheese, and did maggots arise in meat? The argument lasted for many years, and even Lister found it necessary to dispel this false idea which was naturally inimical to his doctrine.

9

One of the first to refute the strange notion was the Italian poet and scientist Francesco Redi, whose book, entitled *osservazioni . . . intorno agli animali viventi che si trovano negli animali viventi* (Observations on living animals which are to be found within other living animals), appeared in 1684. Redi contended that life alone produces life, and that every living thing must have a parent. He noted that maggots do not appear spontaneously in putrefying material, and that if meat is carefully covered so as to exclude flies, no maggots will appear. He also observed that decayed wood or vegetable material did not spontaneously produce bees and beetles and other insects. Thus he produced convincing evidence that the doctrine of spontaneous generation was false, so far as visible creatures were concerned.

Nevertheless there still remained some doubt as to the origin of the smaller forms of life, and the belief that they, at least, could arise by themselves. Spirited discussions took place in all the learned societies of Europe during the eighteenth century.

One of the leaders of the opposition to spontaneous generation was the tireless and ardent Italian priest Spallanzani, while the old view found an equally energetic sponsor in another churchman, Father Needham. Needham showed that a fluid liable to putrefy, any kind of soup, in fact, would still putrefy even in stoppered flasks. Spallanzani, however, was not to be outwitted. He boiled the fluid for an hour, and then sealed the flask. Only when the air was readmitted did the fluid putrefy. It was not innate vegetable force, but little invisible animals, which multiplied by splitting in half, which caused the soup in the flasks to become sour.

A century later the argument was reopened, when the experiments of Spallanzani were repeated by Pasteur and by Lister. The ghost of spontaneous generation was finally laid; it became one of the myths of history.

Putrefaction: Chemical or Vital?

At the beginning of the nineteenth century the question at issue was, whether the putrefaction or fermentation of certain substances was a chemical or a vital process. In 1810, Nicolas Appert, a French confectioner, wrote a book which was translated into English in 1811, under the title, *The Art of preserving all kinds of animal and vegetable substances for several years.* His method was simply to heat the substances and to seal them up in closed vessels so as to exclude the air. Of course Appert was no scientist, but he laid the foundation of the bottling and canning industry, and his work was an important landmark.

A few years later, in 1837, another Frenchman, a chemist named Caignard Latour, demonstrated a curious fact regarding the yeast plant, Torula cerevisiæ, which was later to become a favourite subject of experiment with Lister. Yeast, he showed, was not a chemical substance but a living plant, and it could split sugar into alcohol and carbon dioxide. Moreover, the change could be prevented by the application of heat.

Here, indeed, was a strange phenomenon. Was it merely a chemical reaction, or was it caused by a vital effort on the part of the living plant?

About the same time, Schwann, a physiologist in Berlin, made similar experiments to prove that fermentation was the work of minute living organisms. At this stage the most distinguished chemist of the day, Baron Liebig, stepped in, and added his powerful authority to the view that putrefaction and fermentation could be explained in terms of chemistry. In his view the yeast did not produce those changes until after it was dead.

Liebig's denial that vital agency played any part in the process was the view generally accepted, and there the matter rested for some years, until Louis Pasteur appeared on the scene. Pasteur's wonderful work, and its application to surgery by Lister, will form the theme of a later chapter of this book.

The Contribution of Semmelweiss and Others

Before concluding this preliminary survey of the heralds of Lister's work, it is necessary to mention a pioneer who came very near to the discovery of the antiseptic principle, approaching it from a different angle. The Hungarian, Ignaz Semmelweiss, whose death, after years of frustration and disappointment, took place in 1865, the very year of Lister's discovery, was First Assistant in the Maternity Hospital at Vienna, where every year hundreds of women died after giving birth to their babies.

In 1847 Semmelweiss noted that the cause of those deaths, child-bed fever, or puerperal fever, was really due to infection, and that it was much commoner in the wards devoted to the training of students than in the wards set aside for instruction of midwives. While Semmelweiss was pondering over this observation, his friend Kolletschka, the Professor of Medical Jurisprudence, died from the effects of a scratch received while performing a post-mortem examination. Semmelweiss noticed that the disease which caused the death of his colleague bore a close resemblance to the fever which was such a menace in the Maternity Hospital. "The disease from which Kolletschka had died," he writes, "was identical with that from which I had seen so many hundreds of women die."

Nothing was known of micro-organisms at that time, but Semmelweiss felt convinced that the disease was caused by "putrid material" carried on the hands of students from the dissecting-room to the hospital. He insisted that his students should wash their hands in chloride of lime solution so as to remove the foul odour which, in his view, was the index to the presence of the "putrid cadaveric material" which conveyed the infection. Apparently he believed, as did Lister himself for a time, that infection was always associated with a bad smell. Hence the term putrefaction, a misleading word which remained in use until it was shown that some serious forms of infection, erysipelas, for example, were associated with neither odour (putrefaction) nor with pus (suppuration). Nevertheless the simple ritual of hand-washing in chlorinated solution, suggested by Semmelweiss, led to an immediate fall in the death rate from eighteen per cent. to three per cent.

Fate dealt hardly with Semmelweiss. He felt grieved when his conclusions were not immediately accepted, and he declined to supply further proof and to continue his researches. A disappointed man, he determined to return to his native city of Buda-Pesth. There, he discovered that infection was conveyed not only by the hands but also by bedclothes and dressings, and there, in 1861, he published the book upon which his fame rests, *Die Aetiologie, der Begriff und die Prophylaxis des Kindbettfiebers*, although it received little attention at the time of its publication. His end was tragic. In 1865 he became insane, and he died from infection of one of his fingers. Thus he was a victim of the disease to which he had devoted much careful study.

It cannot be claimed for Semmelweiss that he did more than confirm the observations of his predecessors. Almost a century earlier, in 1773, Charles White of Manchester had drawn attention to the need for scrupulous cleanliness in obstetrics. At the end of the eighteenth century Alexander Gordon had written a *Treatise on the Epidemic Puerperal Fever of Aberdeen* (1795), advising that "nurses and physicians attending patients affected with puerperal fever ought to wash themselves and get their apparel properly fumigated."

Still nearer to the time of Semmelweiss there appeared one of the most important contributions to the problem, and certainly the most eloquent, namely, the paper read before the Boston Society for Medical Improvement by Oliver Wendell Holmes in 1842. He spoke "On the contagiousness of puerperal fever." Dr. Holmes, the Professor of Anatomy at Boston, who was to become at a later day so distinguished in the field of letters, told his hearers that puerperal fever was contagious, and that the doctor in whose practice a case occurred might become a public menace. He regarded the dissecting-room and the post-mortem room as possible sources of infection, and he laid down rigorous rules on the washing of hands and changing of clothes before attending a confinement.

Holmes's teaching was strongly opposed at the time, but the truth of it gradually became evident. He was always rather proud of this early paper, and justly so. Yet he claimed no originality, and fifty years later he wrote that "others had cried out with all their might against the terrible evil before I did, and I gave them full credit for it. But I think I shrieked my warning louder and longer than any of them, and I am pleased to remember that I took my ground on the existing evidence before the little army of microbes marched up to support my position."

The work of those pioneers in the field of obstetrics might well have had its repercussions in surgical practice, but the real cause of the trouble was not understood; consequently, the efforts to prevent or to treat it were merely guess-work, sometimes successful, it is true, but erratic and inaccurate. The problem was still obscure, and so it remained until illumined by the genius of Lister. Lister's demonstration was logical and irrefutable.

It has been essential to mention the work of Semmelweiss and his precursors, as it was alleged by some of Lister's critics that Semmelweiss was the real founder of the antiseptic system, and that Lister owed the idea to him. Lister was obliged to deny the statement, and, although arguments regarding priority were always distasteful to him, he wrote, in 1906, "When in 1865 I first applied the antiseptic principle to wounds, I had not heard of the name of Semmelweiss and knew nothing of his work." Certain it is that Semmelweiss lacked that spirit of research and that infinite patience which led Lister through years of painstaking effort and of hostile criticism to the summit of success.

And now, having prepared the way for Lister by this brief survey, firstly, of the progress of surgery before his time, and secondly, of the evolution of the idea of the infection of wounds by germs, let us attempt to follow his career and to study the process by which he revolutionised surgical practice.

CHAPTER II

EARLY INFLUENCES

THE stranger to London who desires to visit Joseph Lister's early home must pass along miles of mean streets, through Whitechapel, Stepney and Bromley, and across the Essex border. Then he will arrive at Plaistow, now a part of greater London, but in Lister's day a country village five miles east of the heart of the city. There was not even a railway as a connecting link, and those who, like Lister's father, went to London on business, did so on horseback, or driving in a gig or carriage, or as passengers in the daily omnibus to which they were summoned by the blast of the driver's horn.

The house in which Joseph Lister was born is now St. Peter's Vicarage, facing West Ham Public Park. At the time of Lister's birth it was Upton House, a small mansion standing in its own extensive gardens, and what is now the Public Park was the park of Ham House. During the eighteenth century this had been the country home of the famous London physician John Fothergill, the friend of Benjamin Franklin and of many other Americans. Towards the end of the century Anglo-American friendship was sadly strained in the political field, although Americans continued to come to Britain for study.

THE QUAKER COMMUNITY

In Lister's day Ham House was the residence of Samuel Gurney, the banker, and his sister Elizabeth Fry, who did so much to ease the sufferings of prisoners, a class who then suffered more severely than their crimes justified.

Like most of their neighbours, including the Frys and the Gurneys, the Listers were members of the Quaker community. The Quakers, or Society of Friends, have ever been distinguished for their humanity and kindliness. Although they did not approve of "vain sports and places of diversion," so that they took no part in theatre-going, nor in dancing, nor even in music, they were not such doleful killjoys as might be imagined. Owing to their pacifist outlook they could not adopt the army or navy as a career, nor of course could they take holy orders. The majority engaged in trade, and, being thrifty and of simple tastes, and free from the temptations

14

associated with expensive diversions, they often accumulated wealth, which they wisely devoted to the advancement of education and science.

To his Quaker ancestry and upbringing Joseph Lister owed that placid manner and deep human sympathy which endeared him to his patients and to his students, and which carried him to success in the face of many difficulties.

Lister's Ancestry and Parentage

The ancestors of the Listers lived in or near the town of Bingley, in Yorkshire. Joseph Lister, great-grandfather of the subject of this book, left Yorkshire about 1720 to become a tobacconist in London. His youngest son, John, commenced the career of a watchmaker, but gave it up when he succeeded his father-in-law, Stephen Jackson, in the business of a wine merchant. John Lister prospered in business and lived to the age of ninety-eight. One of his letters, quoted in Sir Rickman Godlee's biography, was written when he was fifty-nine to his only son, Joseph Jackson Lister, a schoolboy aged ten. Writing on the 21st day of the third month, 1796 (to retain the Quaker method of dating), the father expresses the hope "that thou may grow up a sober industrious lad," and deplores the fact that the teacher had complained "of thy being very long in writing about 10 lines in a Copy," taking two and a half hours to do what might be accomplished in one hour, "so that thou hast but little time for the Latin, this has made me sorry. . . ." And he goes on to say, "I do desire thee to be in earnest while in the School to apply with industry, that so by overcoming the difficulties thou may begin to taste the sweets of Learning." But probably the boy was more deeply moved by the deprivation of other sweets, announced by his father in a postscript. "We intended to have sent thee a plumb-cake, had we heard a better account but shall now leave it till another time."

Nevertheless Joseph Jackson Lister completed his education satisfactorily, and followed his father in the wine business to such advantage that before he reached middle life he was able to purchase the old Queen Anne mansion of Upton House, and to devote much of his time to his favourite hobby of microscopy.

Seven years before he acquired this property he had married Isabella Harris, daughter of the lady superintendent of the well-known Quaker School at Ackworth in Yorkshire, which had originally been founded by Dr. John Fothergill. Isabella taught in that school with much success; indeed, it became the ambition of visitors to Ackworth to hear her read in public, an accomplishment in which she excelled.

Doubtless Joseph Lister owed much to the wise love and guidance of such a mother, although his biographers have given us more information regarding his father, Joseph Jackson Lister.

As already mentioned, Lister's father gave much attention to the study of microscopy. He used to relate how, as a boy, he became interested in the science of optics when he found that his short sight was improved when he looked through a bubble in the window-pane of his nursery. In adult life he ground his own lenses, like Leeuwenhoek, and after many experiments he discovered that the blurring of the edge of the image could be prevented by a certain combination of lenses in the object glass.

This led to the production of the modern achromatic microscope, and gained for the discoverer the award of the Fellowship of the Royal Society in 1832, an honour which was conferred at a later date on his distinguished son.

Lister's father was thus a man of high attainments and a scientist of note. He was also a good linguist and an excellent artist. His ability with the pencil is shown by the excellent drawings of his wife and of his father, reproduced in Sir Rickman Godlee's *Lord Lister*.

Boyhood Days

Endowed with this excellent parentage, and with the advantages of a happy and prosperous home, Joseph Lister was born on 5th April 1827, the fourth child and the second son. Life held for him none of the struggles against poverty associated with the careers of so many famous men.

In the Quaker School at Tottenham which he attended he received a good grounding in classics and mathematics, while stress was laid upon the writing of essays as a means of developing originality and self-expression. Some of those boyish essays indicate the trend of his thoughts at that early age. There are several relating to osteology, and one on "The Similarity of Structure between a Monkey and a Man." The letter reproduced in Plate I is a proof of his artistic talent, even in childhood.

Before leaving school Joseph Lister had some knowledge of anatomy. Already he had made up his mind to become a surgeon. At this stage, too, he was fond of preparing and mounting the skeletons of small animals. Godlee mentions that at fourteen years of age he wrote as follows to his father: "When Mamma was out I was by myself and had nothing to do but draw skeletons ... and in the evening, with John's help, I managed to

PLATE I

LETTER WRITTEN AT THE AGE OF EIGHT YEARS BY JOSEPH LISTER TO HIS COUSIN. THE ORIGINAL IS IN THE
ROYAL COLLEGE OF SURGEONS OF ENGLAND

Facing page 16

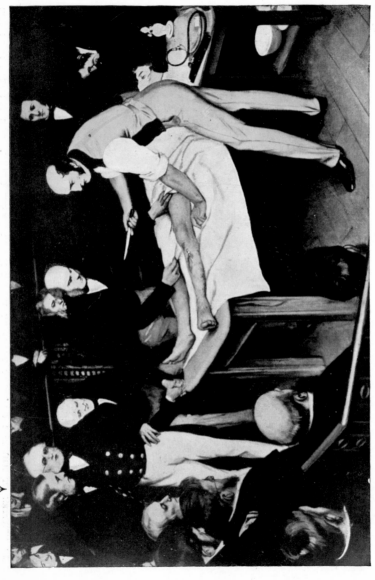

PLATE II

ROBERT LISTON PERFORMING THE FIRST OPERATION UNDER ETHER ANÆSTHESIA IN BRITAIN AT UNIVERSITY COLLEGE HOSPITAL, LONDON, IN DECEMBER 1846. JOSEPH LISTER (INDICATED BY ARROW) WAS A SPECTATOR ON THIS OCCASION

Facing page 17

put up a whole skeleton, that of a frog, and it looks just as if it was going to take a leap, and I stole one of Mary's pieces of wood . . . to stick it down upon and put it on the top of the cabinet with a small bell glass over it, and it looks very nice. Do not tell Mary about the piece of wood."

It was natural that his father, a keen amateur scientist, should wish to foster and promote this love of nature. Joseph Lister owed much to his father's early teaching. Like another great surgeon, John Hunter, he had a keen curiosity for natural history, a road which has led many a boy to the study of medicine. This deep interest he retained throughout his long life, and his holiday diaries are filled with observations on the habits of birds and the distribution of wild flowers. His father was also his chief confidant during those researches which were so close to his heart. To him Joseph sent the first news of his successes, and from him, in turn, drew valuable criticism and encouragement.

Lister the Student

In 1844, at the age of sixteen, Joseph Lister passed from school to university. Little choice was available in this matter. The universities of Oxford and Cambridge demanded an allegiance to the Church of England on the part of their students, so that Quakers and other Nonconformists were denied entrance.

Two years before Lister was born, there had been opened in London a centre of learning which welcomed all comers. University College, it was called, but popularly named "the godless college," on account of its breadth of outlook and its acceptance of all religious beliefs. There Joseph Lister enrolled, and, on the advice of his father, he first studied Arts and graduated B.A. in 1847.

He showed no special brilliancy at this time; indeed he may have found the study hard and irksome. At all events, he suffered a breakdown in mental health through overwork, the result of too early a return to duty after an attack of smallpox. From this he recovered only after a long holiday in Ireland. It would appear that he had become morose and introspective, if one may judge from a letter from his father advising him "not to give way to turning thy thoughts upon thyself nor even at present to dwell long on serious things."

All this dull care vanished as he became immersed in medical study. He was fortunate in his teachers, among whom were several of distinction.

The greatest was William Sharpey, a native of Montrose, who studied medicine and graduated in Edinburgh, then went to Paris, where he met another Edinburgh student who was to become famous—James Syme. Sharpey continued his wanderings for three years, and for the most part on foot, to various Continental centres of learning. On his return, he taught in Edinburgh for a time, and then, in 1836, was appointed the first Professor of Physiology at University College. He was the first in Britain to devote all his attention to this subject. Sharpey took a keen interest in the welfare of his students, and it was he who advised Joseph Lister to visit Edinburgh and see the work of Professor Syme. Sharpey thus determined the course of Lister's career.

Another noteworthy teacher under whom Lister studied in London was Thomas Graham, who had taught chemistry in Edinburgh and Glasgow before his appointment as Professor at University College, and who in later years became Master of the Mint. Graham attained world-wide fame as a chemist, and it is interesting to note that, at that time, chemistry was so intimately associated with medicine that in Glasgow Graham's lectures on chemistry to medical students could not be recognised for purposes of qualification until he had become a Fellow of the Faculty of Physicians and Surgeons.

The Professor of Ophthalmology at University College was Wharton Jones, "a man of small stature, peculiar manner, and an outrageously Scotch accent," but also a philosopher and a man of wide culture. He it was who suggested to Lister that the processes of inflammation might best be studied in the web of a frog's foot, and he fostered in the student a love of research. It was also he who encouraged Lister to publish his first paper, which dealt with the physiology of the eye.

First Publications

In this article, "On the Contractile Tissue of the Iris," which appeared in the *Quarterly Journal of Microscopical Science* in 1853, Lister confirmed the observation of Professor Kolliker of Wurzburg, one of the leading physiologists of the time, that this structure was composed of involuntary muscle; Lister added the information that there were two distinct muscles, one to enlarge, the other to diminish, the size of the pupil.

A second paper by Lister, published in the same year, just after he had graduated M.B. in the University of London, dealt with another subject in which Professor Kolliker was interested, namely, "The Muscular Tissue of the Skin," which produces "goose skin" when in contraction. Both papers were illustrated by accurate drawings by the author. These papers attracted the attention of experts, and must have given great satisfaction to Lister's father, who was so devoted to the microscope.

Even during his holidays young Lister had used the microscope to advantage. In August 1851 he wrote to his father, from the Isle of Wight: "I succeeded pretty well with the shrimps: by getting very small ones and looking at them with the 2/3 glass I saw the heart beating very rapidly, the rapid arterial currents in the limbs, the blood slowly returning over the surface of the limbs and over the back to the heart. . . . We are very happy here. I had a glorious bathe to-day, and swam 52 yards in two minutes."

In surgery Joseph Lister distinguished himself as a student, not only taking a high place in his classes but also showing keen interest in the University College Medical Society, at which spirited debates took place. He became house surgeon to (Sir) John Erichsen, a leading London surgeon and the author of a well-known text-book, and soon after graduating M.B., he added to his qualifications by becoming a Fellow of the Royal College of Surgeons of England.

ETHER ANÆSTHESIA IN BRITAIN

It was at an earlier stage in his student career that Lister witnessed the first major operation to be performed in Britain under ether anæsthesia, by Robert Liston, in University College Hospital, on 21st December 1846 (Plate II). Liston, who had been associated with Syme in Edinburgh before coming to London, was at the height of his fame. The patient on this historic occasion was a butler named Frederick Churchill. The operation was an amputation through the thigh for cancer of the leg, and the limb was removed in half a minute, although such speed was now to be no longer essential. Unfortunately we have no record, either of the result of the operation or of Lister's sensations as he watched it. He must have been deeply impressed, as he was familiar with the terrors of surgery before the introduction of anæsthesia.

Joseph Lister was now twenty-six years of age, and ready to commence practice as a surgeon. Although he had no definite plans, it was assumed that he would settle in London. He decided that before doing so he would visit some of the Continental schools in order to enlarge his experience.

Professor Sharpey, to whom reference has been made, was a teacher who took a keen interest in the progress and welfare of his students. He had marked Lister as one of his brightest pupils for whom the future held a distinguished career. Sharpey therefore had no hesitation in advising young Lister to begin by spending a month in Edinburgh in order to study under his old friend Professor James Syme.

Accordingly, in September 1853, with Sharpey's letter of introduction in his pocket, Joseph Lister set out for Scotland, which was to be his home, not for a month only but for the greater part of his working life.

The Edinburgh School of Surgery before Lister

At this point it may be interesting to sketch the rise and progress of the Edinburgh Medical School before the date of Lister's arrival, and, in particular, to give a brief account of those who upheld the reputation of that centre of learning. To James Syme, who held the Chair of Clinical Surgery, we shall return in the next chapter, as his later career was so closely interwoven with that of Lister. Meanwhile, let us glance at a few of the other eminent teachers who at that time maintained the great traditions of Edinburgh as a centre of medical learning.

The occupant of the Chair of Systematic Surgery was James Miller, an able surgeon and good teacher who had succeeded to the practice of Robert Liston when the latter went to London in 1835. Miller's reputation as an orator served causes other than that of surgical teaching. He was one of the chief spokesmen of the Free Church of Scotland at the time of the Disruption in 1843, and he was also a strong advocate of temperance reform. His *Principles of Surgery*, 1844, had a wide circulation as a text-book, in America as well as in Britain.

He was a close friend of Simpson, and it was with Miller's collaboration that Simpson first used chloroform as an anæsthetic in the Edinburgh Royal Infirmary on 15th November 1847. Between Miller and Syme, however, there was a long-standing feud, and it is recorded that when Miller fell into bad health he called on Syme, determined as he was to effect a reconciliation. Syme was standing before the fire with his hands behind his back when Miller was ushered into his room. Miller said that he had come to say good-bye, but without altering his position Syme replied, "So you've come to apologise, have you? Well, I forgive you." So the incident ended.

The Chairs of Systematic Surgery and of Military Surgery

The Chair of Systematic Surgery had been founded in 1831, and there had been two professors before Miller. The first was John William Turner, an Englishman and an Edinburgh graduate, who died at the age of forty-six.

Before his appointment he had already served for ten years as Professor of Military Surgery, the Chair in this subject having been set up by the Crown in 1806 and occupied by John Thomson, whose remarkable facility for establishing and occupying Chairs earned for him the jocular title, first applied by Dr. Robert Knox, of "the old chair-maker." Originally Professor of Surgery in the College of Surgeons, Thomson became Professor of Military Surgery in the University, and, subsequently, he was the first to occupy the Chair of Pathology when it was founded in 1831, his friend Turner becoming the first Professor of Surgery in the same year.

John Thomson's son, Allen Thomson, was a brilliant young man who in 1848 became Professor of Anatomy in Glasgow, and, later, was a close friend of Lister there. After the death of John Thomson the Chair of Military Surgery in Edinburgh University was occupied by Sir Charles Ballingall, who had seen considerable service in India, as he recounts in his popular *Outlines of Military Surgery*, 1833. On Ballingall's death, in 1855, the Chair of Military Surgery was abolished.

The second occupant of the Chair of Systematic Surgery, Turner's successor, was Sir Charles Bell, who began and ended his career in Edinburgh, his chief work as anatomist and surgeon having been carried out in London. There, he had achieved a great reputation by his researches on the nervous system, and his name stood high as surgeon and scientist when he was called to the Edinburgh Chair of Surgery in 1836. But he was sixty-two years of age, and in failing health. He seemed to realise that his main mission was accomplished, and he wrote in one of his letters that, returning to Edinburgh after thirty-two years' absence, he "seemed to walk in a city of tombs." Six years later he died, and the Chair passed to James Miller.

As for the sister subject of medicine, or the Practice of Medicine as it was called to distinguish it from the Institutes of Medicine, which we now call physiology—this subject, which had ranked so high in the days of William Cullen and of James Gregory, was, at the date of Lister's coming, in the hands of William Pulteney Alison, who had been appointed Professor in 1842, and also Physician to the Royal Infirmary of Edinburgh. Alison had made important contributions to the study of fevers, as well as to the reform of the Scottish Poor Law, and his influence on the progress of public health and of social reform in Scotland was far-reaching, leading as it did to the introduction of legislation in health matters.

But the two Edinburgh professors of that day who shared with Syme an international reputation were Christison and Simpson.

Sir Robert Christison and Sir James Young Simpson

Sir Robert Christison, son of the Professor of Latin in Edinburgh University, had graduated at Edinburgh and had studied in London and Paris. Appointed Professor of Medical Jurisprudence in 1822, he made a great reputation in that field, and he was one of the expert medical witnesses in the case of Burke and Hare. In 1832 he assumed the duties of Professor of Materia Medica, a position which he held with great acceptance for the long period of forty-five years. In his autobiography Christison has left a vivid picture of the life of that time.

Even more widely known was the versatile and energetic Professor of Obstetrics, Sir James Young Simpson. Of humble birth, the son of a baker in the little town of Bathgate, he had been appointed to the Chair in 1840 at the age of twenty-eight, had discovered the anæsthetic value of chloroform in 1847, had built up an enormous practice, and had made valuable contributions not only to his own subject but to other branches of medicine and to archæology, on which he could speak and write with authority.

His forceful and determined manner frequently got him into trouble, and the breach between him and Professor Syme was greatly widened when Simpson presumed to enter the field of general surgery and to argue in favour of his "acupressure" method of checking bleeding by the introduction of long needles.

Lister's difficulties, too, were increased by the opposition of Simpson to the antiseptic system, and by Simpson's view that sepsis was not caused by germs, but was inherent in the hospital building. To this problem we shall have occasion to return in a later chapter.

Others who were at the zenith of their fame when Lister came to Edinburgh were John Goodsir, the Professor of Anatomy who had succeeded the dynasty of three generations of Monros and whose fame was equal to theirs; William Gregory, the Professor of Chemistry, the first to hold that Chair after it had been separated from medicine, a son of James Gregory, who had been Professor of Medicine and the inventor of "Gregory's powder." William Gregory was the first to prepare hydrochlorate of morphia, and it was he who prepared the chloroform used by Simpson in his original experiments.

The Professor of Pathology of that time was William Henderson, who had succeeded John Thomson in 1842. Henderson raised a storm of opposition by his advocacy of homœopathy, and initiated a long controversy in which Syme and Simpson took part, as their views happened to be similar on this occasion.

Those, then, were the leading teachers of the Edinburgh Medical School when Lister came north in 1853. A few notes on the evolution of the school prior to that date may not be out of place.

The University of Edinburgh, or Town's (Tounis) College as it was called, is the youngest of the four Scottish universities. It was not an ecclesiastical foundation, like the Universities of St. Andrews, Glasgow and Aberdeen, each of which was founded by a bishop, the respective dates being 1411, 1453 and 1494. Not until 1583 did the Town Council of Edinburgh take action by founding the College which became the University. So determined was this body to ensure that their new institution should be free from what they called "medieval papistry," that they would not at first apply to it the title of University.

The Royal College of Surgeons of Edinburgh

Long before that date, however, the seeds of anatomical and surgical teaching had been planted by the Barber Surgeons of Edinburgh when they received their charter from the Town Council and from King James the Fourth of Scotland. That was in 1505, and the "Seal of Cause," as it was called, empowered the Incorporation of Barber Surgeons to have the sole right of practising surgery and of examining candidates who might wish to join them. Accordingly, in order that those candidates might be instructed in "the anatomy, nature and complexion of man's body," the guild was entitled to claim each year the body of one condemned criminal, for purposes of dissection or, in the words of the Charter, "ane condempnit man efter he be deid to mak anatomea of quhairthrow we may haif experience."

An additional privilege conceded by the charter was the sole right of making and selling *aqua vitæ* (whisky) within the burgh, a clause which somehow has been allowed to lapse with the passing years. In 1778 the Incorporation of Surgeons and Barber Surgeons became the Royal College of Surgeons of Edinburgh.

We know very little about the lives and work of the early pioneers, and the picture remains hazy until the latter part of the seventeenth century. During this century many British students found their way to Leyden, which was then the medical centre of the civilised world. The torch of medicine, lighted in Greece, had passed by way of the Moslem Empire to Salerno, thence to Montpellier and Padua and Paris, and eventually to Leyden, when it was handed on to Britain and to the New World.

THE ROYAL COLLEGE OF PHYSICIANS OF EDINBURGH

Among the Scottish students at Leyden was Sir Robert Sibbald, eminent not only as physician but as geographer and historian. It was largely owing to his efforts that the Royal College of Physicians of Edinburgh was founded in 1681. Closely associated with him was Dr. Archibald Pitcairne, who came into prominence by championing the cause of William Harvey at a time when few accepted the doctrine of the circulation of the blood.

Pitcairne was appointed Professor of Medicine at Leyden, and among his pupils was his successor Hermann Boerhaave, who became world-famous as a physician and as a teacher, and is regarded by some as the leading physician of all time. Although Pitcairne was a Jacobite and an Episcopalian, and was accordingly unpopular in certain circles, his is a name to be revered in medicine. He greatly furthered the reputation of the schools of Leyden and of Edinburgh.

When he died in 1713, at the age of sixty-one, he left a "jeroboam" of wine which was to be drunk on the restoration of the Stuart monarchy. But as that event was not forthcoming, it was decided, almost a century later, that the restoration of Pitcairne's tomb in Greyfriars Churchyard would prove a sufficient excuse for the opening of the bottle. Accordingly this was done, under the leadership of Professor Andrew Duncan, James Gregory's successor.

BIRTH OF A FACULTY OF MEDICINE IN EDINBURGH UNIVERSITY

Although the teaching of medicine in Edinburgh had been promoted by those Royal Colleges, it was not until 1720 that a Faculty of Medicine was founded in the Town's College. If any one man was responsible for this important event, it was Alexander Monro, called "primus" to distinguish him from his son and grandson, who bore his name, and who, each in his turn, succeeded to his professorial chair.

Monro primus had been specially educated by his father, John Monro, an army surgeon who had studied at Leyden and who determined that an Edinburgh medical school should be modelled on similar lines. With this end in view, he prepared his son for the post of Professor of Anatomy, and the young man, duly appointed, fully justified the confidence thus placed in him.

Alexander Monro primus was not only a distinguished anatomist. He taught and practised surgery, and his son, Monro secundus, who was even more brilliant than his father, became eminent as physician as well as anatomist.

Unfortunately the high standard was not maintained in the third generation. Alexander Monro tertius was content to read from his grandfather's notes written more than a century before, and he did not even omit the remark, "When I was a student at Leyden in 1719," although this passage was regularly greeted by his students with howls of derision.

Monro tertius was succeeded by Goodsir, who revived the prestige of the Chair. But before that time there had been other distinguished teachers of anatomy who held extra-mural classes outside the walls of the University or "College." There was John Barclay, who had so large a following that he was obliged to duplicate his lectures in order to accommodate his class, and who in his enthusiasm was wont to continue lecturing to empty benches after the dismissal bell had been rung. When Barclay died in 1826 there arose the great anatomical star of the period, Dr. Robert Knox. Knox was a born orator and an inspiring teacher, and it is unfortunate that he is remembered chiefly as the recipient of the bodies of the victims of the nefarious Burke and Hare, who in 1829 murdered thirty-five persons in order to sell their bodies for dissection. Knox weathered the storm of abuse with dignity and vindicated his conduct; nevertheless his position and power waned, and he died in obscurity in London.

Anatomy was thus the foundation subject of study in the Edinburgh medical school. In those early days surgery had not emerged as a special subject. Those who practised it were either anatomists like Monro primus or Charles Bell or Robert Liston, or general practitioners like Alexander Wood.

"Lang Sandy Wood," as he was called, was a well-known Edinburgh character at the end of the eighteenth century, when he was a leading surgeon in Scotland's capital city. Tall and spare, he was easily recognised, and if any further means of identification were required, these were supplied by his tame raven and his pet sheep both of which often accompanied him on his professional rounds. He was also the first in Edinburgh to carry an umbrella, which was even then quite a novelty.

The Bell Dynasty

The first in Edinburgh to confine his attention entirely to surgery was Benjamin Bell, "the first of the Edinburgh scientific surgeons." A native of Dumfries, this Benjamin, who was no relation to Sir Charles Bell whose name has been mentioned, was appointed surgeon to Edinburgh Royal Infirmary at the age of twenty-four. Benjamin Bell married Grizel Hamilton, the sister of his friend, Dr. James Hamilton, then a highly esteemed physician of Edinburgh. Bell resided at Liberton, three miles or so from the Infirmary, and he was wont to ride into town on horseback to carry out his surgical duties. He was rapidly attaining success and prosperity, when a fall from his horse almost wrecked his career. For nearly two years he was laid aside and unfit for duty, while "Sandy" Wood attended him and carried on his practice. The long convalescence was well spent in writing *A System of Surgery*, first published in 1783, which remained for many years a highly popular text-book. Benjamin Bell was the first of a dynasty of Edinburgh surgeons, the last being his great-grandson Joseph Bell, who died in 1911. Joseph Bell, to whom we shall refer later as a colleague of Lister, was a well-known teacher of surgery, whose aptitude for diagnosing not only the diseases of his patients but also their occupations and their environment, led one of his students, Conan Doyle, to portray him as the greatest detective of fiction, Sherlock Holmes.

One of Benjamin Bell's assistants was James Russell, who, as we shall relate in the next chapter, became Professor of Clinical Surgery and the predecessor of James Syme. The profound influence of Professor Syme upon the career of young Lister will also occupy our attention in the chapter which follows.

CHAPTER III

LISTER AND SYME

THE Edinburgh to which Lister came was very different from the city which we know to-day. The so-called Industrial Revolution had brought wealth to many centres of industry, and in this affluence Edinburgh had a full share. Although the city was famed for its educational facilities rather than for its manufactures, the commercial advances in other centres of Scotland were naturally reflected in the capital, which, however, had its own busy trades of brewing, papermaking and printing, the staple industries of Edinburgh to this day.

EDINBURGH IN THE MIDDLE OF THE NINETEENTH CENTURY

The expansion of workshops and factories, which the new age of mechanisation had brought, initiated a wave of prosperity throughout the whole country, and in Edinburgh, the seat of the Law Courts and the chief centre of learning; this was shown by the great number of public buildings and private residences which were built at this time. The population of Edinburgh and Leith in 1750 was 60,000; by 1850 it had grown to 200,000; to-day Greater Edinburgh has about 480,000 inhabitants. Originally planned and commenced in 1753, the New Town, with its three great parallel streets—Princes Street, George Street and Queen Street—and the great squares at each end of those mile-long thoroughfares—St. Andrew Square at the east end and Charlotte Square at the west end—had been built before the close of the century. On the high ground to the south, separated from the New Town by the valley now called Princes Street Gardens, stood the Old Town, its single main street, High Street, continued as Canongate, extending as the Royal Mile from the height of the Castle on its rock to the low ground at the eastern end, where stands the Palace of Holyroodhouse. From this central backbone there radiated many subsidiary streets and "closes," the houses of the aristocracy in earlier times. But now, the New Town became the fashionable place of residence and many a county family owned a town-house there.

In the valley beneath the crags of the Castle Hill was the sheet of water known as the Nor' Loch. It might have been worthy of the name of loch had it been allowed to retain its original beauty, but it had become a

27

filthy marsh or bog, a receptacle for dead cats, hanged dogs, cast-off clothing, and all manner of garbage and rubbish. On the east it was bounded by the causeway connecting the Old and New Towns, formed largely from the earth removed in digging the foundation of the latter, and known to this day as The Mound. Eventually the Nor' Loch was drained, but the pleasant valley was to know no peace.

Further changes were imminent. In the opinion of many the fair city was ruined by the railway which found a convenient entrance at this point. In 1842 Edinburgh was joined by rail to Glasgow, in 1846 to Berwick and the South, in 1848 to Carlisle and the South. London, which during the previous century had been reached only after nine days' journey by stage coach, was now accessible by rail in one day. Thus, although the view of the Castle and Old Town from Princes Street might be ruined by the intervening railway line, the improved transport brought many compensations. Of course the Princes Street of that day was largely residential, and there were few of the great shops and warehouses for which it is now famous. Originally a narrower street than it is to-day, with houses on one side and public gardens on the other, it was made still narrower by the cabmen being allowed "to keep their horses' noses well out into the street, ready to have a rush across whenever a hand was held up." Those short sharp races across the street were a source of much amusement. The first to arrive secured the "fare"; there was no queueing then, nor was there any omnibus or tramway or other public transport. The sedan chair had only lately disappeared, one of the last to use it on his professional rounds being Professor James Hamilton, Professor of Obstetrics, who died in 1839.

Princes Street was first publicly lighted by gas in 1822. Indeed, Edinburgh was far in advance of London in the adoption of coal gas as an illuminant. In his *Life Jottings*, Lord Kingsburgh, a well-known Edinburgh judge, born in 1836, recalls that in early childhood he was taken to London, and was surprised to find that the house in which he lived had no gas, but only oil lamps and candles. Long after gas had become universal in Scotland, the practice was slowly copied by England. Meanwhile, a number of painful cases were reported of English visitors to Scotland, who knew nothing of gas, blowing out the flame on going to bed, and being found dead in the morning.

The personal fashions of 1853 would strike the modern observer as very strange. Like all professional men of the time, Lister himself followed the practice of wearing side whiskers and shaving the chin and upper lip, and he wore the tall hat (so convenient for carrying a wooden stethoscope)

Sic dedebat
Sic docebat.
1833

Edin Surgical Hospit Clinents House
Clinical Class 4 March 1833.

A. Peddie

PLATE III

JAMES SYME, AS HE SAT TEACHING HIS CLASS, SKETCHED BY ONE OF HIS
STUDENTS, ALEXANDER PEDDIE, WHO LATER BECAME A WELL-KNOWN
EDINBURGH PRACTITIONER

Facing page 29

and frock coat of the period. Still more remarkable were the ladies' fashions. The crinoline, its ample width increased by folds and flounces and numerous starched petticoats, appeared in 1854, and held its place for about twenty years. It was also the era of the little bonnet so familiar in early portraits of Queen Victoria. Women, young and old, dressed alike, so that all of them looked old.

No doubt all those innovations of building, of transport and of fashion left their mark upon the mind of young Lister. But what impressed him most was the method of teaching surgery and the man who was the master of the method.

THE OLD INFIRMARY

The building known as "The New Surgical Hospital" had only just been opened. It had been built as an extension of the Surgical Section of the Infirmary, originally the High School, but transformed in 1832 from an educational to a surgical institution. The Old Infirmary, of which this surgical block was a part, had been opened in 1742, and it was equipped with seventy-two beds, as well as twelve cells for insane persons. Water was not laid on; it was all carried in buckets. The heating was by fires and the lighting by lamps and candles. By the time the surgical block was added many improvements had been effected, although there was ample need for many more.

The present Royal Infirmary was opened in 1879, and the Surgical Hospital became, first, the Fever Hospital, and later the Engineering Department of the University. It now houses the Department of Geography (Plate XV).

The Old Infirmary, as it came to be called later, was the scene of Syme's great work and of Lister's early labours.

In September, 1853, Joseph Lister arrived in Edinburgh, and, after settling in lodgings at South Frederick Street, presented his credentials to Professor Syme.

PROFESSOR JAMES SYME

James Syme was then fifty-four years of age and at the height of his fame, not only as the leading surgeon of Scotland, but probably the first surgeon of Europe in his day (Plate III). Surgery demanded a cool head and swift judgment, and Syme was gifted with those qualities, and also with a forceful personality. Although he was a man of strong likes and dislikes, and was often engaged in controversy, he always maintained his ground with dignity and uprightness. According to Dr. John Brown, who depicted him so well as the surgeon in *Rab and his Friends*, he "never wasted a word, a drop of ink or a drop of blood." Yet this man of brevity had a gentler side, and many were grateful for his kindly sympathy and his generous hospitality. Born in Princes Street in 1799, the son of an Edinburgh lawyer, or "Writer to the Signet," Syme was essentially an Edinburgh man. He spent all his life in Scotland's capital city, save for a brief period in 1847 when he was called to the Chair of Surgery at University College, London, on the death of Robert Liston, who formerly had been his colleague in Edinburgh. Syme remained in London only a few months as he found the atmosphere uncongenial, and he was glad to be reinstated in his former position in Edinburgh, which had not been filled.

While still a student, he had discovered that naphtha was a solvent for rubber, and that the solution could be used to render cloth waterproof. He might have made a fortune had he chosen to patent the process, but this was done later by Mackintosh of Glasgow, whose name is still associated with the garment.

Early in his career Syme became a popular teacher of anatomy and surgery, although it was not until 1833 that he was appointed to the Chair of Clinical Surgery. The Regius Chair of Clinical Surgery had been founded in 1803 by King George III., twenty-eight years before the Chair of Systematic Surgery was set up in the University of Edinburgh.

The first Professor of Clinical Surgery was James Russell, to whom we have alluded as an assistant of Benjamin Bell. Russell was forty-eight years of age when he was appointed, and his salary was fixed at fifty pounds a year. Elegant in his dress, he wore knee breeches, silk stockings, shoes with buckles, a white cravat, and a red wig. He was not, however, an inspiring lecturer, and Christison, in his autobiography, mentions that Russell was a "somnolent" lecturer, a quality which was accentuated by the hour of meeting of his class, 4 p.m., and by "an inveterate habit the professor had of yawning while he spoke, and continuing to speak while he yawned." Nevertheless he continued to hold the Chair until the age of eighty-one, when he offered to resign on condition that his successor paid him three hundred pounds a year for the remainder of his life, a condition accepted by Syme and fulfilled until the death of the old professor three years later.

On assuming the Chair Syme also was allotted wards in the Old Infirmary of Edinburgh. A few years previously he had been unsuccessful in his application for a vacancy on the staff, and had actually opened, in 1829, a Surgical Hospital of his own, Minto House in Chambers Street, which he conducted with conspicuous success until he was appointed Professor. He then occupied the Chair with great acceptance, and rapidly became the leading surgeon and the most popular teacher of surgery of the day. A vivid and admirable account of James Syme as he was in 1854 has been given by his assistant, Joseph Bell, and it is worth quoting in its entirety.

"When I was a first-year student," he writes, "one of the shrewdest of my father's old friends said to me, 'Stick to Syme,' and so I did. As pupil, dresser, clerk, house-surgeon for two terms, and special assistant surgeon for five years, I stuck to Syme, and no greater teacher of surgery ever lived. He is described to the quick by John Brown in words that are classic, and by many more, yet would I add a stone to his cairn. He was in his fifty-fifth year when I saw him first as a teacher, and he died at seventy; for the greater part of the fifteen years of his late prime I saw him daily. His hospital life was on this wise—two clinical lectures a week, operations two days more (perhaps three), a ward visit when he wished to see any special cases; he spent generally about two hours in the hospital. Driving down in his big yellow chariot, with footman, hammercloth, and C-springs, with two big, rather slow and stately white or grey horses, he used to expect his house-surgeon to meet him at the door and move upstairs with him to his little room, where he at once took up his post with his back to the fire and his hands under the flaps of his swallow-tail coat. In this little room he generally held a small *levée* of assistants, old friends, practitioners wanting to arrange a consultation, old pupils home on leave; and before this select class he examined each new and interesting case that could walk in. The new cases had been collected, sifted, and arranged by the dresser in a little room on the stair, irreverently known as 'the trap,' and Mr. Syme then and there made his diagnosis, which to us young ones seemed magical and intuitional, with certainly the minimum of examination or discussion. One was sent off with a promise of a letter to his doctor, another was fixed for to-morrow's lecture or next day's operation. Then, if it was lecture day, a tremendous rush of feet would be heard of the students racing to get the nearest seats in the large operating-theatre where the lecture was given. Chairs in the arena were kept for colleagues or distinguished strangers; first row for dressers on duty; operating-table in centre; Mr. Syme on a chair in left centre. In his later days it was a fine cushioned chair called the 'chair of clinical surgery.' In 1854 it was a meek little wooden chair without arms. House-surgeon a little behind, but nearer the door; instrument clerk with his well-stocked table under the big window. He comes in, sits down with a little, a very little, bob of a bow, rubs his trouser legs with both hands open, and signs for the first case. The four dressers on duty, and in aprons, march in (if possible in step), carrying a rude wicker basket, in which, covered by a rough red blanket, the patient peers up at the great amphitheatre crammed with faces. A brief description, possibly the case had been described at a former lecture, and then the little, neat, round-shouldered, dapper man takes his knife and begins; and the merest tyro sees at once a master of his craft at work— no show, little elegance, but absolute certainty, ease, and determination; rarely a word to an assistant—they should know their business if the un-expected happens; his plans may change in a moment, but probably only the house-surgeon finds it out; the patient is sent off, still anæsthetised, and then comes a brief commentary, short, sharp, and decisive, worth taking down verbatim if you can manage it, yet he has no notes, a very little veiled voice, and no eloquence. The discipline of the class is perfect, even the idlers are shamed and interested into quietness. Big operations generally used to attract crowds of old pupils, army surgeons, even his colleagues of the medical house. Life in 1854 was not so hurried as in 1892. One fine old physician, who died in 1892, dearly loved a big opera-tion, so much so that Syme used to greet him as 'the stormy petrel of surgery.' Syme was at his best at ligature of large arteries, excisions of tongue, of joints, of queer tumours (which he first had to diagnose and then to get out as best he could), and he was rarely beaten. Of lithotomy he was not a master, and knew it; with the catheter or the stricture staff he was perfect. His hands were too small and his whole physique too dapper to allow him to be brilliant or rapid with the amputating knife at a thigh or a hip-joint. He would not, in 1892, have been considered anything very remarkable, but in 1854 we knew him as the originator of nearly every improvement in surgery of the century."

For some years Syme lived at 9 Charlotte Square, the house which Lister occupied later. In 1842 he acquired the mansion house and grounds of Millbank, a mile or so from the centre of the city and on an attractive site facing the Braid and Blackford Hills and, slightly farther off, the Pentland Hills (Plate IV). There he entertained his friends; there he in-dulged his favourite hobby of gardening, and even in that northern clime he grew orchids and peaches, and even bananas, in the glass houses, which may still be seen, although the house has been demolished to make room for the Astley Ainslie Institution. Latterly he lived at Millbank, while his consulting-rooms were in Rutland Street, close to the west end of Princes Street, then a favourite position for professional premises, also chosen by Lister when he commenced practice. This, then, was the patron from

PLATE IV

"MILLBANK," THE HOME OF PROFESSOR JAMES SYME. IN THE DRAWING-ROOM (ORIEL WINDOW ON RIGHT) LISTER WAS MARRIED TO SYME'S DAUGHTER, AGNES

Facing page 32

J. Wm Beddoe John Kirk George Hogarth Pringle Patrick Heron Watson

Lister David Christison Alexander Struthers

PLATE V

"THE CHIEF" AND HIS ASSOCIATES IN EDINBURGH, 1854

Facing page 33

whom Lister drew much inspiration and encouragement during the early and formative years of his life as a surgeon.

Syme was immediately attracted by this keen and enthusiastic disciple of surgery from London. He received young Lister cordially, and there was rapidly established between the two men a bond of friendship and mutual esteem.

Within a month Lister had accepted the responsible post of "supernumerary clerk" to Syme, and had determined to spend at least the winter in Edinburgh (page 65). About this time we find him writing to his father, telling him that "the stream of surgical instruction and of Syme's kindness continues to flow steadily and, if possible, increasingly. . . . I am more and more delighted with my profession, and sometimes almost question whether it is possible such a delightful pursuit can continue. My only wonder is that persons who really love Surgery for its own sake are rare."

"THE CHIEF" AND HIS DISCIPLES

After spending Christmas at home in London, Lister returned to find that the appointment of resident house-surgeon in Syme's wards had unexpectedly become vacant, and he was invited to accept this post. Here indeed was a valuable opportunity of gaining experience, and Lister was delighted at the prospect, never for a moment considering it beneath his dignity as a Fellow of the Royal College of Surgeons of England to accept an office usually held by a newly fledged graduate. Syme allowed him considerably more scope than was usual, and he was permitted to undertake treatment and to operate, on his own initiative. Twelve students acted as his "dressers." They revered Lister and referred to him as "The Chief," and so he was called throughout his career, while Syme was known as "The Master" (Plate V).

Lister also was fortunate in having, as his fellow students, a band of friendly and genial young men in whose company he worked and played during those happy years. A favourite excursion was the climbing of Arthur's Seat, the hill close to Holyrood Palace. From the summit a fine view of the city and of the Firth of Forth, and even some of the Highland "bens," may be obtained. Close by is the ridge of cliff known as Salisbury Crags, broken at one point by a fissure or chimney up which adventurous youths still scramble. It is called Cat Nick, and has been the scene of many an accident. Lister had a fall there one day while climbing with some of his friends and fellow-residents, including Dr. John Beddoe, who like himself was an Englishman. Beddoe tells the story in his *Memories of Eighty Years*, 1910, and it is a tale worth quoting. Beddoe appears in the group with Lister, reproduced on Plate V.

"If I had killed my friend Lister that summer, which I went near to doing, how much would have been lost to the world and to millions of its denizens. Everybody who has ever been in Edinburgh has seen the long line of cliff called Salisbury Crags. It is like a crescentic tiara, highest in the middle, where it may rise to seventy or eighty feet, and there, oddly enough, is the only place where it is climbable by anybody but an Alpinist. A broad fissure cuts back into the rock from top to bottom, and is called The Cat's (Wild Cat) Nick. I had often ascended by it, and I persuaded Lister that Walter Scott had climbed there (which I believe he had done), and Robbie Burns, and Christopher North, and that in fact it was a feat not to be left undone. So we went thither one day to attempt it. Lister had been overworking himself, and before I, who was leading, had accomplished more than half the ascent, he said to me, 'Beddoe, I feel giddy; would it not be foolish in me to persevere to-day?'

"'Certainly,' I replied, 'let us postpone it till you are in good condition,' and I began to descend. I suppose much experience of the place had made me careless. A large fragment came away in my hands, and the stone and I fell upon Lister. He was looking up at the time, and squeezed himself cleverly against the face of the cliff; but the huge stone struck him on the thigh with a grazing blow, and then fell down the talus below with leaps and bounds, and passed harmless through the middle of a group of children who were playing hopscotch at the bottom, right in its way.

"Lister was badly bruised, but no bone was broken. I went off at once to the Infirmary and procured a litter and four men, wherewith I returned to Lister. As our melancholy procession entered the courtyard of the surgical hospital, there met us Mrs. Porter, the head nurse then and for many years after. She wept and wrung her hands, for Lister was a universal favourite.

"'Eh, Doketur Bedie! Doketur Bedie! a kent weel hoo it wad be. Ye Englishmen are aye sae fulish, gaeing aboot fustlin' upo' Sawbath.'

"I do not suppose Lister ever whistled on Sunday. I am certain I did not, for I never could whistle in all my life; but, we had suffered for the national offence. We were both in bed for a fortnight, at the end of which time, on a Saturday afternoon, up came one of my nurses.

"'Eh, Doketur, can ye no' come doon? Here's Maggie Dixon's ta'en a appleplectic fit, and there's naebody in the hoose tae bleed her.'

"I descended and bled the woman accordingly, and she regained consciousness before I had finished, and made a good recovery. Bleeding is under-rated nowadays. Of course, it was grossly over-valued formerly. Recovered from my bruises, I recognised that I had entirely lost my nerve. It was some little time ere I hit upon the right plan of regaining it. I went to the scene of the accident, and again attempted the climb, and with much shaking and shivering and sweating arrived at the top. Then I undertook the downward climb, which was perhaps worse than the upward one, but that accomplished, the cure was complete."

Syme's famous nurse, Mrs. Porter (Plate VI), who dominated this scene, was the "Staff-Nurse" of whom the poet Henley wrote, while he was a patient in Lister's ward at a later date:—

> "These thirty years has she been nursing here,
> Some of it under Syme, her hero still.
> Much is she worth, and even more is made of her.
> Patients and students hold her very dear.
> The doctors love her, tease her, use her skill.
> They say 'The Chief' himself is half-afraid of her."

A delightful story, which bears out Henley's contention, is told of Mrs. Porter by John Rudd Leeson, a former assistant, in *Lister as I knew him*, and it may be quoted here, although it also belongs to the later period, when Lister had succeeded Syme in the Royal Infirmary of Edinburgh.

"He was fond of ice-bags, and one day the lumps of ice being large, and fearing they might cause discomfort to the patient, he turned them into a towel, went to the fireplace and began pounding them with the poker upon the hearth. Mistress Porter heard the smashing from her lair, and strode excitedly into the ward to learn what it was about; she was quite unabashed by finding it was the Professor himself who was the culprit, and in broad high-pitched Scotch soundly scolded him for soiling her clean hearth. As Henley puts it:

> "The broad Scots tongue that flatters, scolds, defies;
> The thick Scots wit that fells you like a mace.

"Lister desisted at once, and with the quaintest grimace of obsequious submission, literally skipped away. A strange sight indeed, Lister skipping; but it shows he was not devoid of humour in spite of all his seriousness.

"Mrs. Porter seized the towel, bore it off, pounded the ice and brought it back in her left hand, shaking her right fist vehemently at Lister. I forget what she said, but it was an impassioned rebuke that she would not

35

tolerate such conduct, and that he must mend his ways for the future. He bore it with assumed meekness, and with a triumphant air of vindicated justice she withdrew."

Nevertheless Mrs. Porter fairly idolised the two great surgeons in whose wards she ruled, and it is recorded that in her later years she was heard to remark: "We've nae Symes or Listers noo, but we do our little best." This, of course, was long before the days of Florence Nightingale, and although there were some wonderful exceptions, like Mrs. Porter and her colleague Mrs. Lambert, the nurses were by no means well qualified for their duties, and the nursing profession was badly in need of reform.

Although less famous than Mrs. Porter, Mrs. Lambert was quite as strong a character. "Bend the knee, laddie," was her terse remark to a perspiring house-surgeon as he struggled to reduce a fracture of the leg, forgetful of the precept that the muscles might be relaxed by flexing the joint adjoining the seat of fracture!

No one thought of calling Mrs. Porter or Mrs. Lambert "Sister." They would have objected strongly. They were the staff nurses and each of them had thirty-six beds under her care, aided by a drunken old porter and seven so-called night nurses who were responsible also for the scrubbing and cleaning of the wards and passages.

The seventy-two patients under Syme's charge were distributed in six wards and six small rooms. Although the staff nurses were shrewd and capable, though obviously overworked, the nurses, as Joseph Bell has described them, were "poor useless drudges, half charwoman, half field worker, rarely keeping their places for any length of time, absolutely ignorant, almost invariably drunken, sometimes deaf, occasionally fatuous —these had to take charge of our operation cases when the staff nurses went off duty. Poor creatures, they had a hard life! Their day's work began at eleven p.m., when in a mournful procession, each with a blanket round her shoulders, they walked to their wards from a dormitory, so-called, in the east end of the grounds. There they were supposed to keep up the fire and nurse the patients till five in the morning, when they had to set about cleaning the wards, scouring the tins, and preparing for the patients' breakfast.

"During the visit they used to prowl about, and help at the meals of dinner and tea, and it was not till five in the afternoon that they were allowed to trudge back to their dormitory. What wonder that at night they snored by the fire, often on a vacant bed, if they could get one; and, when an accident came in, their blear eyes and stupid heads were of little use, except to rouse up one or two tired house-surgeons to help the one on duty.

"Serious operations were doubled in risk by want of ordinary care, hæmorrhages were unnoticed, amputation cases allowed to rise from bed; indeed, a zealous house-surgeon had his heart nearly broken by their unwisdom and neglect. I know of thirty drops of whisky given in a wine-glassful of morphia, by a night nurse who herself was an opium-eater! The patient was saved by the stomach-pump, but no thanks to her. We could not improve matters by dismissing them, for the candidates for the post were no better; and actually the house-surgeon had to select his night nurses for himself.

"There was no lady superintendent of nurses to help us. The matron was a housekeeper and had kept a baker's shop, and knew no more of real nursing than the poorest of the scrubbers. So when a big operation was over, dressers were called to volunteer; four-hourly watches were told off; and for the first few days certainly the patient was watched, fed, and looked after. In holiday time the poor house-surgeon had his hands full. I have sat up five nights in succession, from four o'clock a.m. till the staff nurse came on, relieving a gallant dresser who took the first half of the night. Just imagine what chance a tracheotomy case would have under such conditions of nursing, unless the students volunteered. We may well be grateful to the wisdom of the managers, and the liberality of the public, which has so far changed all this, so that now each ward has its own skilled trained night-nurse, with a night superintendent to visit her once or twice during her vigil, and every serious operation case has its own special nurse, night and day, when needed."

In the foregoing passage, taken largely from Edinburgh Hospital Reports, 1893, the writer is contrasting the conditions of 1854 with those of 1892, a generation later.

LISTER REMAINS IN EDINBURGH

Only a year after his arrival in Edinburgh there occurred an incident which altered his whole career. R. J. Mackenzie, a young Edinburgh surgeon of brilliant attainments who had assisted Syme and was even mentioned as his possible successor, died of cholera while on military service in the Crimea, and this created a vacancy not only at the Infirmary but also on the teaching staff of the Royal College of Surgeons. Lister naturally sought the advice of Syme, who at first thought he ought to return to London as originally intended. Later, however, Syme changed his mind and determined to support Lister in his application for the post. It was an important step, and Lister discussed it in a long letter to his father, which modestly concluded, "I must not expect to be a Liston or a Syme, still I shall get on. I believe my judgment is pretty sound, which is another most important point. Also I trust I am honest and a lover of truth, which is perhaps as important as anything. As to brilliant talent, I know I do not possess it; but I must try to make up as far as I can by perseverance."

Lister was no recluse, despite his grave and thoughtful demeanour. He loved the simple outdoor pastimes of those Victorian days, and it is also on record that he was fond of music and had a good voice. Wireless and cinemas being then unknown, hosts and guests were wont to entertain each other, and, at Millbank and elsewhere, Lister used to sing Scottish songs, his favourite being "Jock o' Hazeldean."

Thus we find Lister, at the threshold of his career in Edinburgh, engaging Mackenzie's lecture-room at 4 High School Yards, taking a consulting-room at 3 Rutland Street, close to Syme's rooms, and being elected a Fellow of the Royal College of Surgeons of Edinburgh. Before commencing his first course of lectures on surgery he spent a month in Paris, then an important surgical school, and on his return he busied himself with preparations for his lectures and with an important investigation on the problem of inflammation. Knowing that inflammation was the first subject which the teacher of surgery must explain, he determined to make his own observations and reach his own conclusions. Lister was never one who accepted the current view without question. He would see for himself, and accordingly he commenced a series of simple and beautifully designed experiments and microscopical observations which led him steadily towards his greatest discovery. In a letter dated September, 1855, he writes: "I have long wished to see the process of inflammation in the frog's foot, and, as I think I once told thee, felt that the early stages of that process had not been traced as they might be, so as to see the transition from a state of healthy increased redness to inflammation. Accordingly . . . having got a frog from Duddingston Loch . . . I proceeded last evening to the investigation . . . and a most glorious night I had of it." He goes on to describe the alteration and the calibre of the blood-vessels and the slowing of the blood current produced by hot water, mustard and other irritants, and he concludes, "I cannot of course give thee a full account of the numerous interesting facts that turned up in the course of the evening; suffice it to say that the experiments were all successful. I am half inclined to give my opening lecture on inflammation; but I shall see in a few days. . . . Mr. Syme says by way of encouragement that after the first plunge I shall get on well enough." The subject of his first lecture, on 7th November 1855, was inflammation, and he described the circumstances in a letter to his brother Arthur, thus: " . . . of the 21 foolscap pages of close writing of which my Introductory consisted, three only were written on the morning of the third day (the Quaker term for Tuesday). I went to bed at 2 on the 4th day (Wednesday) morning, and rose at 4, after half an hour's sleep, and got the last words written just in time to go off in a cab to read them. . . . I have already seven pupils entered. I cannot yet at all tell how many will ultimately enter, as many do not take out their tickets till a week or a fortnight. . . . The way I manage to work is by getting up early, I go to bed at 10 and get up by alarm at 5.30, light my fire, and my coffee boils while I dress. I take it and a bit of bread, work for three or four hours, and off to my 10 o'clock lecture when my mind is brim full of it." Lister was not at all depressed by the small number attending his class. He gave them of his best, and the impression he left with them was deep and lasting. If Lister had any fault it was that of unpunctuality and of leaving the preparation of lectures to the last moment. This did not arise from any indolence, but rather from his becoming so deeply immersed in the work on hand as to forget the passage of time.

His father gave good advice in a letter: "I admire the morning plan and hope thy early bed hour may enable thee to keep to it. But was it not running too great a risk and tempting failure in thy first lecture to delay till so late its preparation? An example of what is to be avoided hereafter?" Still, the lecture, with its record of original researches, was highly successful, and it formed the foundation of two papers entitled, *On the Early Stages of Inflammation*, which Lister read before the Royal Society of London in 1857. He showed how the changes of colour in the skin of the frog in varying environments were due to a concentration or a diffusion of the pigment granules. It may seem curious that a surgeon should have concerned himself with problems of physiology which had no apparent bearing upon the practice of surgery. But as time went on, the association became increasingly obvious, and in later years Lister remarked with truth that physiology was as important to the surgeon as to the physician.

Joseph Lister was now firmly established as an Edinburgh surgeon, and before he commenced his second series of lectures in November, 1856, he had been appointed Assistant Surgeon to the Royal Infirmary.

THE DEVOTION OF AGNES SYME

Another important event took place that year. On 23rd * April 1856 Joseph Lister was married to Agnes Syme, Syme's eldest daughter, in the drawing-room at Millbank, according to the old Scottish custom. By taking this step of "marrying out," Lister was obliged to sever his connection with the Quaker community. Naturally this caused some regret to one of so sensitive a nature, but he laid little stress on the formalities of religion, and from the communion of the Scottish Episcopal Church he derived peace and satisfaction throughout the remainder of his life.

In Agnes Syme, Lister had found an ideal partner. She was accomplished and vivacious, a charming hostess and a thoughtful and devoted wife. In all his work she showed the keenest interest, writing for hours to his dictation (there were no typewriters in those days), attending to his instruments and assisting in his experiments. Lister owed much to his wife, who deserves to share in the success which she did so much to promote. The Listers had no children, but theirs was a union of perfect accord and happy companionship which lasted for thirty-seven years, until it was broken by the death of Lady Lister while they were on a holiday at Rapallo in Italy.

After their wedding, the Listers spent a month at the English Lakes and at Upton, and then set out on a three months' tour of Europe, visiting many of the medical schools and meeting some of the most distinguished surgeons, of Pavia and Padua, Vienna and Prague, and so on to Wurzburg, Leipzig and Berlin. It was an excellent introduction to a great career. On returning to Edinburgh they made their home at 11 Rutland Street, where an inscription on the wall of the house records the fact that Lister lived there. It is now rather a dingy little street of offices, overshadowed by the "Caledonian" railway station. But it was conveniently near the fashionable residential quarter, and within twenty minutes' walk of the Infirmary. Lister was now a very busy man. It may be true that he had little private practice, and that Mrs. Lister was justified in referring jocularly to "poor Joseph and his one patient," but his time was fully occupied by his work at the Infirmary, his class of Surgery and his continued researches, now directed towards the Coagulation of the Blood, on which he contributed a series of papers to various scientific societies.

In 1859, Professor Lawrie, who occupied the Chair of Surgery in Glasgow University, was about to retire owing to ill health. Lister was

* The date is given as 23rd (Godlee), 24th (Cameron), and 25th (Dukes), but the first-mentioned is accepted as probably the most authoritative.

PLATE VI

MRS. JANET PORTER (1810–1890) WHO WAS ASSOCIATED WITH SYME AND
WITH LISTER, AND WHO SERVED FOR FORTY-SEVEN YEARS AS NURSE IN
THE ROYAL INFIRMARY OF EDINBURGH

Facing page 40

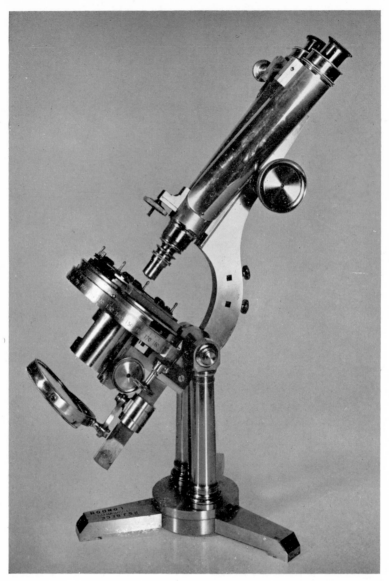

PLATE VII

LISTER'S MICROSCOPE, NOW PRESERVED WITH OTHER LISTER RELICS IN THE
MUSEUM OF THE ROYAL COLLEGE OF SURGEONS OF ENGLAND. THE FAMILY
OF BECK, MAKERS OF THE INSTRUMENT, WERE RELATED TO LISTER

Facing page 41

urged to become a candidate for this post. There were seven applicants, five from Glasgow and two from Edinburgh, and Lister was finally selected. He was regarded as a man of great promise, a good teacher, and an original thinker. To leave Edinburgh, in which he had spent seven very happy years, was in some respects a trial to Lister, and also to his wife, who was now to be separated from her old home. Nevertheless there was in Glasgow, with its industrial population, even greater scope for surgery than in Edinburgh, and Lister was the first surgeon there to limit his practice entirely to surgery. Already Lister had good friends in Glasgow. There was Gairdner (afterwards Sir William), the Professor of Medicine, and Allen Thomson, who held the Chair of Anatomy, while in other Faculties were distinguished men such as Lushington, Professor of Greek, and Thomson (later Lord Kelvin), Professor of Physics.

To his dismay Lister discovered that he must deliver a Latin thesis on assuming the Chair, and in writing to his father he tells how "by Aggie's suggestion I took a Latin dictionary with me in a small carpet bag," and how he completed the work on the railway journey between Edinburgh and Glasgow. All passed off well, however. He was warmly welcomed by his new colleagues and, as he continues in the same letter, "had just comfortable time to take the 5 o'clock train for Edinburgh." The induction of the new professor took place on 9th March 1860, and a few weeks later, after being entertained to a banquet by his Edinburgh students and accepting the gift of a silver flagon, Lister removed to his new home at 17 Woodside Place, Glasgow.

The most important epoch in his career, marked by his discovery of the antiseptic principle, was passed in Glasgow. Although he did not know it at the time, his preparation for this vast accomplishment could not have been bettered, even if the future had been known. His was not a career which commenced in a log cabin or a mean street; from earliest years his income was always sufficient for his needs. He had experienced the great advantage of a happy home, a sound education, inspiring teachers, and ample facilities for his surgical work. In addition he was now blessed with the companionship of a devoted wife, and he had been appointed to one of the most important Chairs of Surgery in the country. This ample share of good fortune naturally smoothed his path of progress; nevertheless much hard work, steady application, self-confidence, and refusal to accept discouragement were needed in the great task to which Lister now addressed himself.

CHAPTER IV

THE ANTISEPTIC PRINCIPLE

GLASGOW in 1860, the date of young Professor Lister's arrival from Edinburgh, was by no means the "second city" of Britain as we know it to-day, with a population of well over a million (1,120,000 in 1946). In 1865, the nearest date of which accurate figures are available, the population of Glasgow was 470,000, or approximately the same as that of present-day Edinburgh. Before the eighteenth century, Glasgow was quite a small town. In the sixteenth century it held only the eleventh place among Scottish towns, and it did not outstrip Edinburgh in size until about a hundred years ago. The growing trade with America in the early days of the eighteenth century brought great prosperity to the port of Glasgow, which challenged the supremacy of Bristol in the tobacco trade, and which enjoyed almost a monopoly in the importation of sugar and molasses. The wealthy Glasgow merchants built handsome mansions and the town extended rapidly. Then came the period known as the Industrial Revolution, the introduction of steam navigation, the development of the coal fields and iron foundries of Lanarkshire, and the rapid rise of all manner of manufactures which gave to Glasgow a position of high importance in the world of commerce. Throughout the nineteenth century the population rapidly increased, almost doubling itself in the first twenty years of the century.

As the city grew and expanded, it was natural that education should keep pace with industry. Glasgow has never been lacking in intellectual prowess. When the University was founded by Bishop Turnbull in 1453, no provision was made for the teaching of medicine. There may have been efforts to introduce it into the curriculum, as we learn from Andrew Boorde the adventurous English traveller, priest and physician, who wrote, in 1536: "I am now at a little unyversite named Glasco where I study and practise physyk for the sustentacyon of my lyving." Boorde was the author of *A Breviarie of Health*, the first original medical work in the English language to be printed in England. Dated 1543, it is now one of the greatest prizes of collectors of early books.

THE PIONEER WORK OF MAISTER PETER LOWE

The next important landmark in the march of medical progress in Glasgow was provided by Maister Peter Lowe, who, after studying abroad, and wandering for twenty years as a surgeon with the armies of France and Spain, returned to his native town of Glasgow about 1596, and published his *Discourse on the Whole Art of Chyrurgery*, the first text-book of surgery to be written in English, which remained a deservedly popular work for many years (Plate VIII).

Peter Lowe died in 1612, and his tomb, which may still be seen in the Cathedral churchyard, bears the following quaint epitaph:—

> Ah me I gravell am and dust
> And to the grave deshend I must
> O painted piece of liveing clay
> Man be not proud of thy short day.

But the most enduring memorial of Peter Lowe was the "Faculty" which he founded. In 1599 Peter Lowe secured Royal Assent to the foundation of a Faculty of Physicians and Surgeons which would regulate and control practice in Glasgow and neighbourhood. Prior to this date, Royal Colleges of Physicians and of Surgeons had been established at London and at Edinburgh, but the Faculty founded in Glasgow was the only corporation in which the physicians and surgeons had united in their efforts. The Faculty was empowered to decide who was qualified to practise, to impose a fine of 40 pounds Scots upon any of their Fellows who "profaned the Sabbath by working on that day," and to provide free treatment for the poor, in other words, "to give counsel to puir disaisit folk gratis." The last-mentioned function is still observed in spirit if not in practice, as the Minutes of all meetings of the Faculty to this day conclude with the words "The poor were treated gratis and the Faculty adjourned."

The power to control medical and surgical practice within their area remained in the hands of the Faculty until the introduction of the Medical Register in 1858.

The Faculty, which became the Royal Faculty in 1909, was never a teaching body, and it was not until the eighteenth century that an attempt was made by the University to establish medical education by appointing, first, a Professor of Medicine in 1714, and second, a Professor of Anatomy and Botany in 1720. Neither of those gentlemen appears to have taken his duties seriously; indeed, one historian refers to them as "the inert professors."

WILLIAM CULLEN, FOUNDER OF THE GLASGOW MEDICAL SCHOOL

The real founder of the Medical School of Glasgow was William Cullen. Born at Hamilton, Lanarkshire, in 1710, he served his apprenticeship to a Glasgow surgeon, made a voyage to the West Indies, assisted a London apothecary and then commenced practice in his native town along with another Lanarkshire man, William Hunter. Shortly afterwards, Hunter removed to London, there to become eminent as an anatomist and obstetrician, and to be joined by his younger brother, John, one of the foremost surgeons of all time. Cullen continued to practise in Hamilton for a few years. But a genius and energy so great as his demanded a wider horizon. To be the founder of a medical school at Glasgow similar to that of Leyden, or that which had been founded at Edinburgh in 1720 by Alexander Monro, was his supreme ambition, and with this object in view he removed to Glasgow in 1744. All teaching was interrupted in the following year, the year of the fateful '45 Rebellion in which the romantic Prince Charles Edward was the leading figure; but in 1747 Cullen was appointed the first lecturer on Chemistry in Glasgow University.

William Cullen was not content to teach only chemistry in the Glasgow "College," as the University was then called. He lectured also on botany, on materia medica and on the practice of medicine. He was, in fact, as has been said, "a medical faculty in himself," and he also conducted a busy practice.

There was no clinical or bedside teaching at that time, and although a small Town Hospital at Glasgow Green had been opened in 1733, it was not until 1794, four years after Cullen's death, that the Royal Infirmary of Glasgow opened its doors.

In 1751 Cullen was promoted to the Chair of Medicine at Glasgow, and in 1755, after he had been teaching in Glasgow for eight years, he was called to Edinburgh as Professor of Chemistry and Physick.

In Edinburgh, his worthy service to medical education continued, and that city is proud to unite with Glasgow in doing him honour as one of the great pioneers.

Our reminiscences of the Glasgow School of Medicine have led us far from Lister, but it is necessary that we should have a clear picture of the scene in which Lister was to accomplish the most important step in his great achievement.

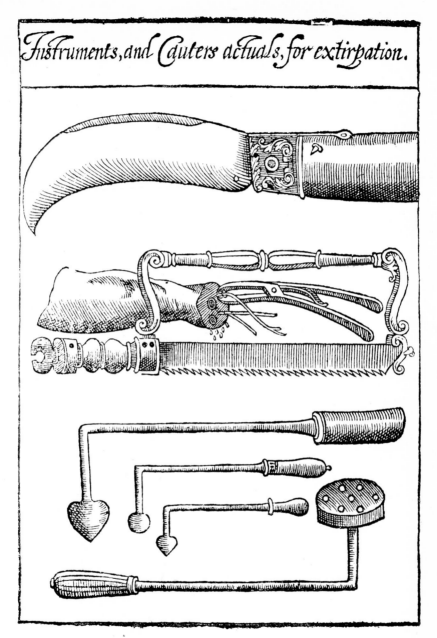

PLATE VIII

EARLY INSTRUMENTS FOR AMPUTATION, FROM "A DISCOURSE ON THE WHOLE ART
OF CHYRURGERY," BY PETER LOWE, 1596

Facing page 44

PLATE IX

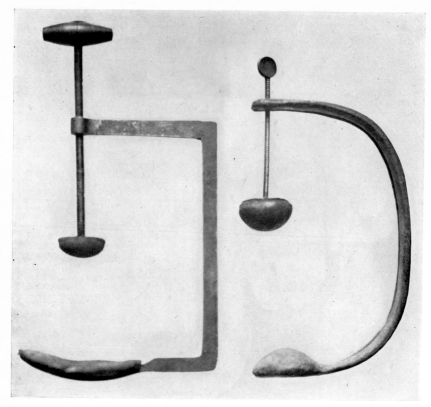

LISTER'S ABDOMINAL TOURNIQUET

TOURNIQUET FOR ABDOMINAL AORTA (ONE-THIRD NATURAL SIZE)

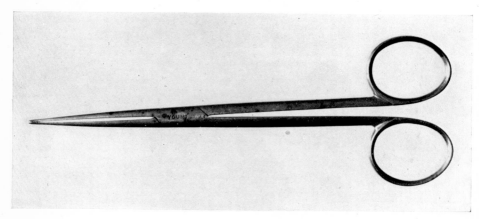

LISTER'S SINUS FORCEPS

SINUS FORCEPS (NATURAL SIZE)

THE REGIUS CHAIR OF SURGERY IN GLASGOW

The Chair of Surgery, which he had been called to occupy, was established in 1815, and the first professor was John Burns. Burns had already taught anatomy, midwifery and surgery at the extra-mural school, known as the Andersonian University. This institution, designed by John Anderson, Professor of Natural Philosophy in Glasgow University, and founded after his death in 1796, was intended as an opponent and as a stimulus to the University. Only the faculties of medicine and of arts were formed, although it was originally intended that law and theology should be included. In 1877 the name of the institution was altered to Anderson's College. The Medical Faculty was especially successful, and was a valuable recruiting ground from which the University drew many of its professors.

Among them was John Burns, who was a popular and successful teacher of anatomy, surgery, and midwifery at Anderson's College before he was called to be the first Professor of Surgery in the University of Glasgow. This was one of the four new Chairs established by the Crown, the other three being those of Midwifery, Botany, and Chemistry. Appointed to this post in 1815, John Burns served the University well until his death in 1850. He was drowned when the steamer *Orion*, on which he was travelling, was wrecked on the Wigtownshire coast.

Burns was succeeded in the Chair of Surgery by James Adair Lawrie, who also had been a lecturer in Anderson's College. On the death of Lawrie in 1859, at the age of fifty-eight, Joseph Lister was appointed to fill the vacancy.

LISTER COMMENCES WORK IN GLASGOW

Although Burns and Lawrie had held, each in his time, the appointment of Surgeon to Glasgow Royal Infirmary, the Chair of Surgery did not entitle its holder to a hospital appointment, so that more than a year elapsed before Lister was placed in charge of wards at the Royal Infirmary (Plates X and XIV). In the interval of waiting, however, his days were fully occupied.

It was at about this time, too, that Lister invented a number of ingenious surgical instruments, including a needle for silver wire which was then in use for stitching wounds; a screw tourniquet for compressing the abdominal aorta, the largest blood-vessel of the body; a hook for the removal of peas, beads, and other objects from the ear; scissors with blunt probe-shaped points for cutting a bandage or stitch without pricking the patient; and slender forceps which could enter narrow sinuses and be used for a variety of purposes.

45

No instrument designed by Lister is better known than his sinus forceps. This instrument is six inches long, with ring handles like scissors and very slender blades, the blunt points having transverse grooves on their opposing surfaces. Lister used to demonstrate that with a pair of those forceps he could pick fluff out of the smallest key. The catalogues of makers of surgical instruments still include Lister's ear hook, his sinus forceps and his scissors, although the tourniquet and needle have become obsolete. If he had made no other contribution to surgery, the name of Lister would still be remembered for these ingenious improvements and innovations in tools and technique (Plate IX).

In the Library of the Royal College of Surgeons of England there is a letter which is worth quoting, relating to the tourniquet which Lister invented. Writing to Lister in 1862, to thank him for the loan of an abdominal tourniquet, Professor James Spence of Edinburgh, who apparently had retained his sense of humour although he was known to his students as "Dismal Jamie," adds the following P.S. to his letter: "Do you think you could get a Glasgow bailie to submit to a trial of the compressor (after dinner) as a complete test of its powers and after-effects: this of course is merely a suggestion.—J.S."

The duties of the Chair of Surgery at Glasgow involved a daily lecture, which meant for Lister much careful preparation, as his lectures were by no means a repetition of current views on surgery, but rather the outcome of deep study and original thought.

Another form of preparation consisted in the renovation and re-seating of the lecture theatre, which Lister carried out at his own expense. His class of Surgery numbered 182, the largest number of students in any course on surgery at that time. When there were added to the duties of the Chair those of a chief surgeon to the Infirmary, the new professor must have lived laborious days. Nevertheless he found time to devise an operation for the treatment of tuberculous disease of the wrist joint—excision of the wrist— which obviated the necessity of amputation. Lister was always keenly interested in conservative surgery, and he considered that "to save a human hand from amputation, and restore its usefulness, is an object well worthy of any labour involved in it." The operation, which remained in vogue for some years, was difficult and tedious, but Lister's results were encouraging, and when the extensive surgical practice of the Infirmary gave him opportunities to improve his technique he was able to describe in *The Lancet* a series of fifteen cases. The paper *On Excision of the Wrist for Caries* is a model of clear reasoning and accurate observation.

A Grateful Patient

Sir Hector Cameron, who had been Lister's house-surgeon in 1866, and who had remained his ardent disciple, has related that when he unveiled the statue of Lord Lister in Kelvingrove Park, Glasgow, in 1924, an old lady stepped forward and modestly requested to be allowed to place a wreath at the foot of the statue. She had been a patient in Lister's ward many years previously, as a girl of twelve years, when Lister had operated upon her wrist and had given her a useful arm. Never had she forgotten his kindness, and now, at the age of seventy-one, she had come to pay her small tribute to his memory.

This fine bronze statue, close to that of Lord Kelvin, represents Lister in academic dress, seated, and looking across the River Kelvin to the Art Gallery on the opposite bank. It is a worthy monument, in a picturesque setting. On the lovely hilltop site behind it, Gilmorehill, stands the University, although Lister did not teach there, as it was not until 1870 that the Old College in the centre of the city was vacated, and the University established in its present premises.

At the end of Lister's first session in Glasgow his students took the unusual course of presenting him with an address in which they recorded their high appreciation of his teaching. The member of the class chosen to read the address was Mr. J. B. Russell, who afterwards attained eminence as the first full-time Medical Officer of Health for Glasgow. Many years later, recalling the occasion in the course of conversation with Sir Hector Cameron, Lister said: "When you find your fellow-students think so well of a comrade as to select him to perform an important and representative task, you may be sure that you will find him, years afterwards, holding a high position in his profession. Watch his career, and you will seldom be disappointed."

Lister was not a prolific writer. He never wrote a text-book, but his contributions to medical journals are all well worthy of study by surgeons even at the present time when many of the methods described by Lister have become obsolete.

Shortly after his arrival in Glasgow he was asked to contribute to the comprehensive four-volume *System of Surgery* (1860-64), edited by Timothy Holmes, articles on Amputation and on Anæsthetics. Lister was the only contributor outside of London to this important treatise. In the former paper he mentions the method of amputating at the ankle joint devised by Syme, and the various other procedures which were in vogue at that time, when amputation was much more frequently practised than it is to-day.

Lister's Contribution to Anæsthesia

As for anæsthetics, his remarks apply entirely to the use of chloroform. The anæsthetic properties of this drug were discovered by Sir James Y. Simpson in 1847, and it had taken the place of ether, the general anæsthetic first used in this country by Liston some months earlier. Lister stated that "Mr. Syme has given chloroform about five thousand times without meeting with a death, and Sir J. Simpson's experience has been equally satisfactory." He also speaks of the "unlimited confidence in this agent by the inmates of the Edinburgh Infirmary." Of course he does not deny that deaths may occur, but he attributes them to "an overdose of this potent narcotic."

Chloroform was at that time administered on a folded towel, the precise quantity being a matter of little consequence so long as free access of air was allowed. In Lister's view, the nature of the respiration was the key to the successful administration of chloroform. The pulse might be disregarded entirely, but the breathing must be carefully watched, and the anæsthetic withdrawn, if there was the least departure from normal respiration. Death from chloroform "is almost invariably due to faulty administration."

Lister had the great advantage of entering the practice of surgery at the time of the introduction of "man's greatest single gift to suffering humanity," as Osler called it. The surgeon was no longer obliged to confine his cutting to a few moments, in his attempt to lessen the duration of the patient's agony. He might now proceed with greater care and deliberation, exploiting the new possibilities which had been placed within his reach, and devising new operations of an extent and duration previously impossible. Nevertheless there remained the dread menace of septic infection which anæsthesia did nothing to mitigate. The actual operation might be perfectly and painlessly conducted, but within a few days the wound usually became inflamed and suppurating, and the patient and his surgeon found themselves fighting what proved very often to be a losing battle. It does not surprise us to learn that the death rate was even greater after the use of anæsthesia became the usual practice.

The Menace of Septic Infection

The local suppuration of the wound was often the least of the dangers to be faced. General infection was common, and it assumed various forms. One of the most frequent was septicæmia or blood poisoning, a disease

PLATE X

GLASGOW HOSPITALS, OLD AND NEW

PRINT DATED 1802, SHOWING THE ROYAL INFIRMARY OF GLASGOW, OPENED IN 1794. THE BUILDING WITH BELFRY, ON THE LEFT OF THE STREET, IS THE HOSPITAL OF ST. NICHOLAS, DATING FROM 1471

Facing page 48

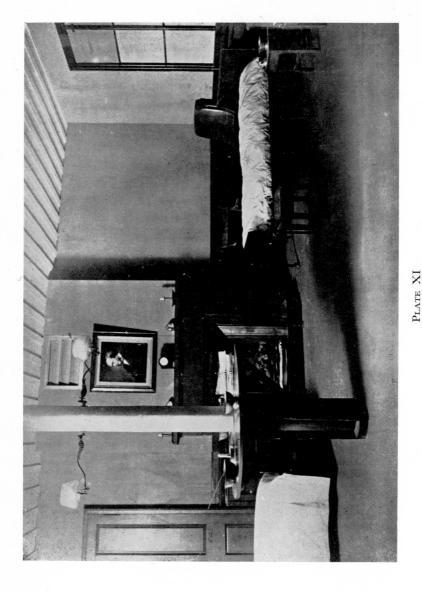

PLATE XI

LISTER'S MALE ACCIDENT WARD IN THE ROYAL INFIRMARY OF GLASGOW, THE SCENE OF HIS INVESTIGATION
AND DISCOVERY OF THE ANTISEPTIC SYSTEM OF WOUND TREATMENT

Facing page 49]

still existing to-day, although very seldom now as a sequel to operation. Erysipelas was another complication very common after operative or accidental wounds. It spread with epidemic violence and caused many deaths. Again, the infection might take the form of pyæmia, a disease associated with the formation of abscesses in various parts of the body, often distant from the wound. Pyæmia was very common, and the death rate was high. Another complication, perhaps less frequent but much dreaded and extremely painful, was tetanus or lockjaw, for which there was no cure at that time. Most feared of all was a disease which is now unknown. It was called Hospital Gangrene, and it took the form of local death of the tissues around the wound, which became grey or black. The process spread rapidly and many deaths were due to this disease, which occurred only in the surgical wards of hospitals and spread from patient to patient.

Writing in reminiscent vein many years later, Sir Hector Cameron, who had been Lister's house-surgeon in Glasgow, stated that he had seen no fewer than five cases of pyæmia following amputation for injury die in the male accident ward in one week, while other cases of this disease and of hospital gangrene lay ill in the same ward.

Such experiences produced in the minds of many surgeons, including Lister, a sense of discontent and of frustration, but the majority accepted the situation with resignation, regarding it as inevitable and uncontrollable. Denonvilliers, the leading surgeon of Paris, said, in 1870, "When amputation seems necessary, think ten times about it, for too often, when we decide upon operation, we sign the patient's death-warrant"; but this negative advice was all that he could offer.

It does not surprise us to learn that at least one-third of the cases of amputation died, and that the majority of surgeons resorted to operative treatment only in circumstances of urgent necessity. Besides amputation, the commonest major operations were ligations of large arteries for aneurism, removal of stone in the bladder, and the excision of tumours. The danger of septic complications imposed a drastic restriction upon the activities of the surgeon, and greatly narrowed his field.

SURGERY IN LISTER'S STUDENT DAYS

At the time to which we refer, only about two hundred operations a year were performed at the hospital in which Lister had studied—University College Hospital, London. In the majority of hospitals only one operating-theatre was available. It was used on only one day in the week,

D

and the blood stains beneath the sawdust sprinkled on the wooden floor remained as a semi-permanent memento of the surgeon's work. In theatre and wards there was not even that ordinary cleanliness upon which we now insist, although we demand a surgical purification which is much more than the mere removal of domestic dirt.

The ritual of "sterilising," which is now applied to dressings and instruments, to the hands of the surgeon and to the skin of the patient, was almost entirely neglected at the time of Lister's discovery, although his first effort at combating the evil was to insist on frequent hand-washing and to provide piles of clean towels in his wards. Even this was neglected by many surgeons. Some of them wore in hospital dirty old coats or jackets no longer fit for street wear, and in performing a dressing or operation they did not always remove them or even turn up the sleeves. Through one of the buttonholes there was often threaded a wisp of silk ligatures in readiness for use.

As for the instruments, these received the most perfunctory cleaning. Probes and scissors passed freely from patient to patient, from wound to wound, as also did the communal sponge, which was often grossly polluted and never surgically clean.

The Cause and Cure of "Hospitalism"

Such was the condition of affairs when Lister assumed charge of wards in that part of the Glasgow Royal Infirmary known as the New Surgical Hospital. Great disappointment had been experienced when it was found that even in the new building, septicæmia and other dire complications continued with undiminished frequency, and the frightful mortality was as large as ever. Although the cause was unknown, one fact was clear and evident, namely, that the septic scourge was more prevalent in hospitals than in private houses. It was more widespread in the towns than in the country, while the largest hospitals suffered most. This observation had been made by many surgeons. As early as 1801, John Bell, in his *Principles of Surgery*, had pointed out that the only hope for patients suffering from hospital gangrene was to remove them from hospital, to "hurry them out of this house of death," to "lay them in a schoolroom, a church, or even a stable," in fact to "carry them anywhere but to their graves."

It was Sir John Erichsen, of London, in whose wards Lister was house-surgeon, who first coined the word "hospitalism," and attempted to prove that the trouble arose "in the very fabric itself." The only remedy, in his view, was to demolish and to rebuild the hospitals. A somewhat similar opinion was expressed by Sir James Young Simpson, whose distinguished career as an obstetrician and as the discoverer of the anæsthetic properties of chloroform ensured for him a ready audience. Simpson was a gifted scholar, with a dynamic, if somewhat dogmatic, personality. In his forcible style he had asserted that the patient on the operating-table was exposed to greater danger than the soldier on the field of Waterloo, and he advised that hospitals should consist of collections of small and inexpensive buildings which could be pulled down and re-erected at intervals. Simpson's contention, supported by statistical evidence, was widely accepted, and led to a revolution in methods of hospital construction. Nevertheless the measures directed against "the fabric itself" failed to eradicate the scourge of sepsis.

The condition of Lister's wards in Glasgow Royal Infirmary when he assumed control in 1861 was no better than elsewhere, and was indeed rather worse (Plates XI and XIV). A scandalous state of affairs was disclosed when it was discovered that the new surgical block had been built on the site of a cemetery in which thousands of victims of a cholera epidemic had been buried in no great depth of soil only twelve years previously. It is difficult to imagine a more unhealthy site, and, as Lister himself wrote, in words which displeased the Infirmary directors and led to an unfortunate argument in the public Press, "The wonder was, not that these wards upon the ground floor had been unhealthy, but that they had not been absolutely pestilential."

This was the scene of the first success of Lister's antiseptic system, "at a time when the unhealthiness of other parts of the same building was attracting the serious and anxious attention of the managers." The annual cleaning of his wards was even omitted because "as those wards continued healthy, it had seemed unnecessary to disturb them."

Lister intended nothing disrespectful to the managers in pointing out the obvious defects of the environment in which he worked. He merely wished to emphasise that his system might be successfully applied even in unfavourable surroundings, and he was justified in his claim: "None of my wards ever assumed the frightful condition which sometimes showed itself in other parts of the building, making it necessary to shut them up for a time." The success of the antiseptic system put an end to all talk of "hospitalism."

THE PROBLEM OF WOUND INFECTION

We do not know how long Lister pondered the problem of wound infection before he made the first experiments which led to his discovery.

51

Even in the early Edinburgh days it claimed his attention, and we have evidence of this in an anecdote related long afterwards by Sir John Batty Tuke, who had been one of his dressers, in a letter to Lister, dated 14th March 1907. "Did I ever tell you of my recollection of you in 1854 (or 1855) when extending, at your dictation, Mr. Syme's lectures one night late, you somewhat suddenly said, 'Let us go and look at that popliteal case.' You took down the dressing, and found the wound healed except where the ligature was. You said, 'The main object of my life is to find out how to procure this result in all wounds. But why is it not healed around the ligature?' Boy-like I said, 'The irritation of the silk.' 'No,' you replied, 'not of, but *in* or *on*.'" This incident appears to suggest that Lister had pondered the problem of sepsis for ten years before making his discovery.

One reason of Lister's success in a field in which others had failed was that he had taken the trouble to study all the sciences which had any bearing upon surgery.

"Physiology," he said, "is even more important to the surgeon than to the physician." His knowledge of chemistry was essential to his researches, and so was his familiarity with biology which he owed to his father. He was never a mere technician. For him, surgery was not only a handicraft, it was an art and a science.

The Healing of Wounds

As was written in the first chapter of this book, the treatment of wounds had undergone little alteration throughout the centuries of recorded history. Two methods were now in use: the dry dressing, favoured by Syme, and the water dressing, popular on the Continent and employed by Liston. There is evidence to show that Lister at first used both methods, according to the needs of the case.

Healing by "first intention" was quite unusual; the majority of wounds healed by "second intention," the wound cavity gradually becoming filled with "granulations" and the skin edges growing in, with the usual accompaniment of suppuration, so that whether the dressing was wet or dry at first it very soon became soaked with pus. It was even a common practice to place a zinc tray under the stump of the limb after amputation, to receive the discharge which steadily dropped from the wound.

Another mode of healing had been described by the famous eighteenth century surgeon, John Hunter, namely, healing under a scab, but this result could be hoped for only in superficial wounds. The original description is worth quoting. John Hunter writes:

"Where the parts are not brought together, so as to admit of union by the first intention, nature is always endeavouring to produce the same effect. The blood which is thrown out in consequence of the accident and which would have united surfaces brought in contact, is in part allowed to escape, but by its coagulation on the surface a portion is there retained, which drying and forming a scab, becomes an obstacle to suppuration. The inflammation in this case may be greater than where union can be effected, but not nearly so great as when suppuration takes place."

*   *   *   *   *

"This might be considered as the first mode of healing a wound or sore, for it appears to be the natural one, requiring no art, and in the state of parts before mentioned, the complete union is in some degree indebted to this mode of healing, by uniting the edges that were not or could not be brought into close contact by means of a scab; proper attention to this has, I believe, been too much neglected. Many wounds ought to be allowed to scab in which this process is now prevented; and this arises, I believe, from the conceit of surgeons who think themselves possessed of powers superior to Nature and therefore have introduced a practice of making sores of all wounds; as a scab, however, must always be on a surface, it is only on superficial wounds that scabs form."

Lister was a keen admirer of John Hunter and was familiar with his writings. "Why," he asked himself, "was this excellent natural process of healing under a scab so frequently rendered ineffective by the presence of suppuration?" The answer, in Lister's own words, was that "the essential cause of suppuration in wounds is decomposition, brought about by the influence of the atmosphere upon blood or serum retained within them, and, in the case of contused wounds, upon portions of tissue destroyed by the violence of the injury." At first, Lister seems to have shared the common belief that the entrance of air into wounds caused all the trouble. Fortunately he was interested in the entire field of medicine and in the contiguous fields of various sciences. Thus he could view the subject of his enquiry from many angles.

The key to the problem was to be placed in his hands by a chemist, as the following chapter will explain.

CHAPTER V

THE CLUE AND THE DISCOVERY

W HILE Lister was pondering the problem which has been outlined in the previous chapter, his colleague Thomas Anderson, the Professor of Chemistry, drew his attention to the work of Louis Pasteur, which supplied the essential clue. Pasteur was at that time a distinguished chemist. He had been awarded the Rumford Medal of the Royal Society in 1856 for his researches in crystallography, and now he had turned his attention to fermentation in wine and had proved that it was not a chemical process, as Liebig had thought, but was caused by minute living organisms or germs which were widely disseminated in the air. Furthermore, he showed that the fermentation of wine, of milk, or of butter was in each case the work of a special germ or organism.

The Experiments of Pasteur

Pasteur proved his contention by boiling decoctions of yeast in a number of long-necked flasks which could be sealed by melting and drawing out the glass. The fluid remained unaltered and remained so indefinitely. When the flasks were afterwards unsealed by breaking the neck, air rushed into the partial vacuum. Pasteur found that such of his flasks as were opened thus in dusty city rooms at once became contaminated, so that the fluid rapidly putrefied and decomposed, while in those which were opened in the purer air of the Alps (actually on a glacier, the Mer de Glace) it showed no alteration at all. To a wondering audience in Paris, on 7th April 1864, Pasteur showed his flasks of sterilised broth, four years old, still clear and unfermented. "I wait, I watch, I question it, asking it to repeat, before my eyes, the wonder of creation. But it remains silent, silent ever since I began the experiments years ago; silent because I have kept it away from the germs in the air, kept it away from life."

Experiments of an even simpler nature were carried out by Lister. He boiled urine in a series of flasks, some of them having straight necks, others necks bent and twisted at various angles. Into those having straight necks dust entered readily and the fluid decomposed, but as the dust was trapped in the curves and angles of the other flasks, the fluid remained germ-free and did not decompose (Plate XII).

Those flasks of Lister's became classical, and were used repeatedly at many lectures. He and Mrs. Lister carried them to London and elsewhere on frequent occasions, balanced carefully on their laps in cabs and railway carriages during the journeys. Those two sedate passengers, so tenderly nursing their flasks, must have provided a source of amusement to their fellow-travellers.

Lister had at once recognised in the original experiments of Pasteur the evidence which was lacking in his solution to the problem of suppuration. Clearly, Lister argued, it was not the air alone which caused the trouble, although other surgeons, fearing the entrance of air into the wounds which they treated, had attempted to seal the wounds in order to exclude the air, using collodion and other substances for this purpose.

Now, however, as Pasteur had shown, it was not the air but rather *something in the air* which produced fermentation in certain fluids. Was it not possible that those minute organisms, or "germs" as they were called, were the cause of putrefaction in wounds? If the blood clot, which was Nature's dressing, could be prevented from putrefying, then all those dreaded complications might be avoided. Thus did Lister arrive at his discovery as he read the writings of Pasteur, and as he realised that putrefaction in wounds might well arise from the same cause as fermentation in wine. He concluded at once that there had been "a flood of light thrown upon this important subject by the philosophic researches of Monsieur Pasteur."

Pasteur had said that "without theory, practice is but routine born of habit, for theory alone can bring forth and develop the spirit of invention." Lister was greatly impressed with the work of Pasteur, and throughout his life he never ceased to acknowledge the debt he owed to him. The discoveries which had been so well applied by Pasteur, the chemist, in studying the fermentation of wine, were now to be transferred by Lister, the surgeon, to the prevention of putrefaction in wounds.

THE GERM THEORY SUPPLIES THE CLUE

"The germ theory of putrefaction," said Lister in a lecture in 1868, "is the pole star which will guide you safely through what would otherwise be a navigation of hopeless difficulty." On another occasion he said: "You must be able to see with your mental eye the septic ferments as distinctly as we see flies and other insects with the corporeal eye. If you can, you will be properly on your guard against them." At this time neither Lister nor anyone else had seen the micro-organisms which cause suppuration. Many years were to pass before Lister was able to produce full proof in support of his contention. What he saw with his mental eye as he studied Pasteur's writings was a sufficient basis for his experiment. In a letter now preserved in the Royal Faculty of Physicians and Surgeons of Glasgow, written from London to Dr. G. H. Edington in December, 1902,Lister remarks, "It was not until after I went to Glasgow that bacteria and other microbes claimed my attention. All efforts to combat decomposition of the blood in open wounds were in vain until Pasteur's researches opened a new way, by combating the microbes." But even after he accepted Pasteur's findings, Lister had no idea that germs could gain access to the body in any other way than by being conveyed in the air to open wounds. That, however, was sufficient. He must discover some means of preventing the entrance of germs into wounds, "by applying as a dressing some material capable of destroying the life of the floating particles."

THE ANTISEPTIC VALUE OF CARBOLIC ACID

It was clearly impossible to kill the germs by means of heat as Pasteur had done in his experiments with the flasks. Some chemical substance must be used. Lister tried sulphite of potash and other substances, with little satisfaction at first. Then he noticed in the newspapers that carbolic acid had been used with excellent results as a means of purifying sewage at Carlisle, where it had been also noted that this substance destroyed the entozoa which were parasitic on cattle, grazing in the neighbouring pastures. Lister obtained a sample, and used it in his first experiments. It was a sticky malodorous fluid, known also as German creosote, almost insoluble in water but freely soluble in oil. A purer substance was soon obtained, and this became more freely available when the manufacturing chemist, Frederick Calvert, established his works at Manchester in 1865.* Calvert's carbolic acid was less irritant and caustic than the crude carbolic acid and was soluble in twenty parts of water.

Carbolic acid had already been in use as one of those numerous antiseptic substances applied by surgeons in an indiscriminate fashion. It had been brought into prominence as a cure for all manner of diseases by Jules Lemaire of Paris, who in 1863 had published a book entitled *De l'Acide Phénique: de son action sur les végétaux, les animaux, les ferments, les venins, les virus, les miasmes, et de ses applications à l'industrie, à la hygiène aux sciences anatomiques et à la thérapeutique.*

Lemaire had no definite course of procedure, and appeared to recom-

* Calvert first began to manufacture carbolic acid in 1857.

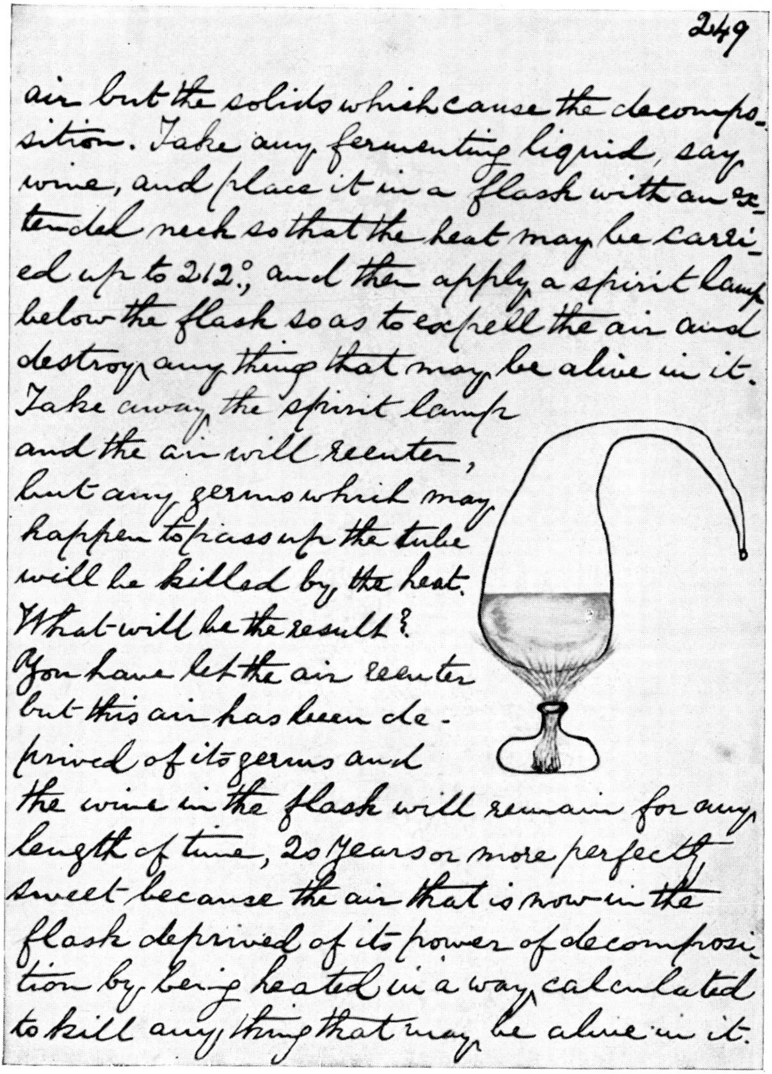

air but the solids which cause the decomposition. Take any fermenting liquid, say
wine, and place it in a flask with an extended neck so that the heat may be carried up to 212°, and then apply a spirit lamp
below the flask so as to expell the air and
destroy any thing that may be alive in it.
Take away the spirit lamp
and the air will reenter,
but any germs which may
happen to pass up the tube
will be killed by the heat.
What will be the result?
You have let the air reenter
but this air has been de-
prived of its germs and
the wine in the flask will remain for any
length of time, 20 years or more perfectly
sweet because the air that is now in the
flask deprived of its power of decomposition by being heated in a way calculated
to kill any thing that may be alive in it.

PLATE XII

NOTES TAKEN BY W. S. ANDERSON, ONE OF LISTER'S STUDENTS AT GLASGOW.
LISTER DESCRIBES HIS EXPERIMENT IN SUPPORT OF THE ANTISEPTIC PRINCIPLE

OBSERVATIONS

ON THE

Diſeaſes of the Army.

BY

JOHN PRINGLE, M.D. F.R.S.

The Third Edition enlarged.

APPENDIX,

CONTAINING

EXPERIMENTS

UPON

Septic and Antiseptic Subſtances;

WITH

Remarks relating to their Uſe in the Theory of Medicine:

Read at ſeveral Meetings of the Royal Society.

EX SIMPLICITATE DECUS.

LONDON:

Printed for A. Millar; D. Wilson; and T. Durham, in the Strand; and T. Payne, next the Mew-gate, near St. Martin's Church. MDCCLXI.

Plate XIII

TITLE-PAGE OF THE THIRD EDITION OF SIR JOHN PRINGLE'S "DISEASES OF THE ARMY," WITH APPENDIX DEALING WITH "SEPTIC AND ANTISEPTIC SUBSTANCES." THE APPENDIX DOES NOT APPEAR IN THE FIRST EDITION OF 1752, BUT WAS ADDED LATER mend carbolic acid indiscriminately—as a preservative of food, as a para-siticide, as a deodorant, and so on; and in his book of 750 pages he devotes only a few lines to the use of carbolic acid as a wound dressing. Neverthe-less the critics of Lister's principle, and especially those critics who imagined that Lister claimed to have discovered carbolic acid, were quick to point to the work of Lemaire and to accuse Lister of merely following the Frenchman's lead. An anonymous letter, which appeared in the public Press and which accorded priority of discovery to Lemaire, was believed to have been written by Sir James Young Simpson, the eminent obstet-rician of Edinburgh, who had discovered chloroform anæsthesia in 1847. On another occasion Simpson alluded to Lister and his "mythical germs." Now, Lister had never even heard of Lemaire, and as for carbolic acid, it was only one part of his antiseptic system.

Misuse of the Term "Antiseptic"

It was the use, or rather the misuse, of the word "antiseptic" which had misled those critics. The word was not in common use even then, although Thomas Carlyle, a few years previously, had referred to certain men as "useful antiseptic products of their generation," in the same fashion as modern youth applies the converse term "septic" in a derogatory sense to persons or things indiscriminately.

One of the first to use the word in the true scientific sense was Sir John Pringle, in a paper in the *Gentleman's Magazine* for 1751, dealing with "Experiments on Bodies which resist or promote Putrefaction in Animal Substances." To such "bodies" he applied the adjectives "antiseptic" and "septic." Pringle was Chief Medical Officer to the army which was sent to quell the Jacobite Rebellion in Scotland in 1745, and he was present at the Battle of Culloden. His chief claim to fame, however, was his suggestion, during a previous campaign, at the Battle of Dettingen in 1743, that hospitals should be regarded as sanctuaries, and should be respected by both belligerent parties. This idea was developed later by Henri Dunant when he instituted the organisation known as the Red Cross Movement in 1862.

It is, however, Pringle's use of the words septic and antiseptic which concerns us at present. Of course he had no idea of the reason of the action of drugs used as wound dressings, like so many others who used antiseptics before that term came to be applied (Plate XIII).

The close association of carbolic acid with Lister's name was unfortu-nate. One still hears him described as "the man who used carbolic acid."

Now, it cannot be too strongly emphasised that the use of carbolic acid was merely a part of his technique for the avoidance of sepsis. If Lister had chosen to call his method the germ-free method or the sterilising method, instead of the antiseptic method, there probably would have been less misunderstanding of his aim. The leading idea of the antiseptic method or system was not the use of a new drug or dressing. It was rather, to use Lister's own words, "the systematic employment of some antiseptic substance so as to prevent the occurrence of putrefaction, as distinguished from the mere use of such an agent as a dressing."

When, in course of time, the use of heat as a means of destroying germs displaced to a large extent the use of antiseptics such as carbolic acid, the aseptic method, as it was called, was simply another means of attaining the end which Lister had shown to be necessary. Stephen Paget stated the matter very neatly when he wrote, "We call the one method antiseptic, and the other aseptic; but we might easily reverse these two adjectives without damage either to the proprieties of grammar or to the values of surgery. They are both applications of the same principle."

The Antiseptic Method on Trial

An attempt has been made to convey to the reader some of the ideas which Lister had in mind as he constructed the principle upon which his discovery was to depend. We have now reached the stage at which he was ready to put it to a practical test. It was natural that he should first apply his method to the treatment of compound fracture, which differed so remarkably from simple fractures in which the skin remained unbroken. The latter healed quickly and satisfactorily, the former placed the patient in danger of his life and, at last, led to the loss of a limb, amputation being the usual treatment. The famous London surgeon of the previous century, John Hunter, had made a similar observation in regard to fracture of the ribs. If a broken rib penetrated the lung so that air escaped into the tissues, no suppuration occurred, but if it was forced through the skin, suppuration was inevitable. This puzzled John Hunter, but as no one presumed the existence of germs, he could only say that "there must be another cause," something more than the air, to account for this strange difference of behaviour in fractures. Lister, as we have seen, demonstrated the truth of the "germ theory" by means of his flasks. It was obvious to him that the simple fracture resembled the flask to which germs could not gain access, while the compound fracture corresponded to the flask which was freely open to germ-laden air. Perhaps, by excluding the

PLATE XIV

ROYAL INFIRMARY, GLASGOW

THE NEW SURGICAL BLOCK OF GLASGOW ROYAL INFIRMARY, OPENED IN 1861. LISTER'S WARDS WERE A MALE ACCIDENT WARD, NO. 24, ON THE GROUND FLOOR TO THE LEFT OF THE ENTRANCE DOOR, AND A FEMALE SURGICAL WARD, NO. 25, ON THE FLOOR ABOVE, TO THE RIGHT OF THE ENTRANCE. THE WARDS WERE DEMOLISHED IN 1924, A PROCEDURE WHICH CAUSED CONSIDERABLE CONTROVERSY germs from the wound and killing any which had already gained access, a compound fracture might be rendered as harmless as a simple fracture.

THE CRUCIAL TEST

The first case to be treated, in March, 1865, proved a failure, "in consequence," as Lister modestly states, "of improper management," but that did not deter Lister from continuing his investigation.

Some months elapsed before another suitable case became available. Of this historic case Lister wrote as follows: "On 12th August 1865, a boy named James Greenlees, aged 11 years, was admitted to the Glasgow Royal Infirmary, with compound fracture of the left leg, caused by the wheel of an empty cart passing over the limb a little below its middle. The wound, which was about an inch and a half long and three-quarters of an inch broad, was close to but not exactly over the line of fracture of the tibia. A probe, however, could be passed beneath the skin over the seat of fracture and for some inches beyond it. Very little blood had been extravasated into the tissues." Such was Lister's description of the first of a series of eleven cases of compound fracture treated between that date and April, 1867. The treatment consisted in a thorough application of undiluted carbolic acid to all parts of the wound, which was then dressed with lint or calico soaked in the same fluid. The dressing was covered with a sheet of tinfoil to prevent evaporation. Mixed together, the blood and carbolic acid formed a scab or crust which did not putrefy, and under the protection of which the wound steadily healed after the manner described as blood-clot healing by John Hunter many years before.

Ten more cases of compound fracture were treated, and all recovered life and limb save two. One patient, a labourer whose leg had been fractured by a kick from a horse, contracted hospital gangrene at a time when Lister was away from home for several weeks, and it became necessary to amputate the leg, after which he recovered. There was only one fatality in the series, a quarryman whose thigh had been fractured by a fall of stone, who made good progress for some weeks and then died from hæmorrhage caused by the perforation of the main artery by a sharp fragment of bone. The remaining nine patients made remarkable recoveries, and while still engaged in this epoch-making experiment Lister wrote to his father: "There is one of my cases at the Infirmary which I am sure will interest thee. It is one of compound fracture of the leg, with a wound of considerable size and accompanied by great bruising, and great effusion of blood into the substance of the limb, causing great swelling. Though hardly expecting success, I tried the application of carbolic acid to the wound to prevent decomposition of the blood, and so avoid the fearful mischief of suppuration throughout the limb. Well, it is now eight days since the accident, and the patient has been going on exactly as if there was no external wound, that is, as if the fracture were a simple one."

Antiseptic Putty and Lac Plaster

Having secured such excellent results in cases of compound fracture, Lister next turned his attention to the treatment of abscess. Tuberculous disease of the spine was a common disease, and it often gave rise to a large abscess which followed the course of the psoas muscle into the thigh. Neither Lister nor anyone else at that time knew that the abscess was caused by micro-organisms, and Lister himself wrote that "in an un-opened abscess no septic organisms are present, so that it is not necessary to introduce the carbolic acid into the interior. Here the essential object is to guard against the introduction of living particles from without, at the same time that a free exit is afforded for the contents." This end he secured by making an incision in the abscess under the protection of a piece of calico dipped in a solution of one part of carbolic acid in four parts of linseed oil. After a number of experiments he found that instead of the oily antiseptic rag, a satisfactory application was a mixture of carbolic acid, linseed oil and common whitening. This he called antiseptic putty. It was spread on tinfoil in a layer a quarter of an inch thick, and was changed daily. The putty used in abscess "proved valuable in simplifying the treatment of compound fracture."

Lister's first printed announcement of his discovery appeared in *The Lancet* in 1867, under the title, "On a new Method of treating compound fractures, abscesses, etc." A year later he contributed to the *British Medical Journal* a paper "On the antiseptic system of treatment."

Lister very soon discovered that carbolic acid caused considerable irritation. He therefore sought for some substance which might be placed next the wound, to act as a "protective." Tinfoil and gold leaf were tried and found wanting. Then, after numerous experiments, he found that oiled silk coated with copal varnish answered the purpose very well.

Thus it was possible to secure the joint action of "an antiseptic to exclude putrefaction, and a protective to exclude the antiseptic."

In order to improve upon the disadvantages of "carbolic putty" Lister made trial of many forms of plaster, and eventually he announced in a paper to the Medico-Chirurgical Society of Glasgow, in 1868, that he had found a substance to answer his requirements. This was a mixture of carbolic acid and shellac, spread on calico and coated with a solution of gutta-percha. The "lac plaster" remained in use until 1870, when Lister began to use absorbent dressings. At about the same time as lac plaster was introduced it was found that a one in twenty watery solution of carbolic acid was "sufficient to destroy the putrefactive organisms," and it was therefore introduced in place of the undiluted acid.

THE PROBLEM OF THE LIGATURE

Much had already been achieved when, in October, 1867, Lister wrote to his father that "surgery is becoming a different thing altogether." There were, however, many problems awaiting solution. Chief among them was the arrest of hæmorrhage. Now at that time, in order to control bleeding, it was the practice to pick up the ends of the severed blood-vessels with forceps, and to tie them with silk threads or ligatures. The ends of the ligatures were left long, and were left hanging out in a bunch at one end of the wound. As healing progressed, each ligature "came away," but the process was attended by the inevitable suppuration, and sometimes, if the wall of the vessel was eroded, by severe bleeding, demanding a repetition of the ligation. Moreover, the ligatures were sources of irritation and they tended to prolong the suppuration. Lister knew, as indeed he had told his dresser, Batty Tuke, ten years earlier, that the source of irritation was "in" the ligature. He believed that a germ-free ligature might be safely left in the wound, and he determined to explore this possibility by animal experiment. Accordingly, on 18th December 1867, at the Glasgow Veterinary College, he tied the carotid artery of an old horse, using a piece of silk cord which had been soaked in carbolic acid. He cut the ends short and closed the wound, which healed by first intention. Six weeks later the animal died of old age, and on examination the silk was found unchanged, imbedded in fibrous tissue.

Lister now felt justified in applying his method to the human subject, and the opportunity came when he had occasion, a month later, to ligate a large artery, the external iliac, in a lady of fifty-one years who suffered from aneurism of the femoral artery. He took the precaution of steeping the silk in pure carbolic acid for two hours before using it, and the operation proved a complete success.

On 5th February 1868 Lister wrote to his father: "I send just a few lines to give thee what I know will be the welcome news that the case of ligature of the external iliac continues to do as well as can be wished. I have seen the patient this morning, six days after the operation, and she is as if nothing had been done to her." Lister was impressed and delighted with this case. One of the chief obstacles to the application of his antiseptic method had been surmounted. Nevertheless he was not completely satisfied, as he realised that the silk, which remained unabsorbed, might give rise to irritation. In one of his early cases of compound fracture he had made two remarkable observations. He noted, firstly, that the blood clot which gave protection to a healing wound might actually become incorporated in the healing tissues, and secondly, that a foreign body in a wound, such as a fragment of dead bone, might become eaten up and thus disposed of during the process of healing. He therefore sought next for some animal substance which might be used as a ligature instead of silk but might possess the added advantage of becoming absorbed.

The Introduction of Catgut

Various materials had been tried, such as leather and tendon, but Lister decided that catgut, prepared from sheep's intestine, might prove more suitable. Again it was necessary to carry out a test by animal experiment, and while spending a Christmas holiday at home at Upton, in 1886, he operated upon a calf, using his father's museum as an operating-theatre. Having administered chloroform to the animal, he tied the carotid artery in two places with catgut. His nephew, who became Sir Rickman Godlee and who wrote the standard biography of Lister, was his assistant at the operation. The calf made a rapid recovery, and when it was sacrificed in the interests of science a month later the original catgut had been replaced by living tissue.

Many experiments were made by Lister before he discovered a method of preparing catgut for surgical use. For some years a carbolised catgut preserved in oil was used by many surgeons, who carried it as part of their equipment, and it proved very satisfactory. The problem of the catgut ligature continued to occupy Lister's attention almost to the end of his long life, and four years before his death he wrote a paper, describing the process of preparing "sulpho-chromic" catgut for surgical purposes. It is interesting to recall that in 1870, while he was still experimenting with carbolised catgut, he learned from an old fiddler who used to amuse the patients in the Royal Infirmary of Edinburgh, that catgut was sensitive to changes in the weather, especially when it was not sufficiently old and seasoned for use.

Acupressure

Sir J. Y. Simpson had also been aware of the disadvantage of the old form of ligature, and had introduced another method of avoiding ligatures altogether and of checking bleeding by the temporary introduction of long needles which compressed the vessels, thus obviating the need for ligatures. This he called Acupressure, and he wrote a large book in support of this new method. By this incursion into the realm of surgery Simpson incurred the wrath of his colleague Syme, who, it is said, strode into his classroom one morning carrying the pamphlet in which Simpson had described this new method, which he had named Acupressure. Calling for an amputating knife, Syme cut the offending paper to shreds. "That, gentlemen," he said, "is what I think of acupressure." It was natural, therefore, that Simpson did not approve of the catgut ligature, and his animosity towards Lister did not lessen when catgut won the day and acupressure was no more.

The history of the Edinburgh Medical School had been frequently punctuated by polemics of this nature. Joseph Lister was not one of those who loved to argue. The atmosphere of argument was distasteful to one of so sensitive a temperament. His patience must have been sorely tried by those who misunderstood him, but his replies to his critics were never bitter. He contented himself with pointing out that his principle consisted in "the systematic employment of some antiseptic substance so as to prevent the occurrence of putrefaction, as distinguished from the mere use of such an agent as a dressing." The method was naturally more successful in the hands of those who had taken the trouble to study it at first hand, than with those who merely "gave the thing a trial." Visitors, especially from the Continent, began to frequent Lister's clinic in Glasgow. Lister, who was a good linguist, would talk to them fluently in French or German, as occasion demanded. From London in those early days came William MacCormac and Marcus Beck; from Denmark, Saxtorph; from Paris, Lucas Championnière. These visitors found that here was a complicated technique which demanded study, and that only those who fully understood the principle upon which the new method was founded could hope to secure results comparable to those of the discoverer.

In the foregoing account of Lister's discovery no mention has been made of his kindness and consideration for his patients, which was unbounded. They, in turn, adored and revered him, and trusted him implicitly. The familiar doll story related to an incident during the Glasgow period. Here it is, as told by one of his house-surgeons:

"A little girl was suffering from an abscess of the knee. As Lister came to her bed he greeted her with his accustomed and delightful smile. They understood each other perfectly, and he dressed the joint.

"When all was finished she produced her doll which had lost a leg; a fumble under her pillow brought out the limb, and holding dolly in one hand and the leg in the other, gravely handed them to Lister. With seriousness and concern he received the case, shook his head ominously, for it was very serious, fitted them together, asked for a needle and cotton, and carefully and securely stitched on the limb, and with quiet delight handed her back to her mother. Her large brown eyes spoke endless gratitude, but neither uttered a word."

Further light is shed upon this incident in a letter, now in the possession of the Royal College of Surgeons of England, from Agnes Lister to her sister-in-law Mary Godlee. It is written from 17 Woodside Place, Glasgow, dated 4th March 1868, and a noteworthy feature is the Quaker style of address which is adopted in the first sentence.

MY DEAREST MARY,

I fear thee must be thinking me very negligent in having let so many days pass since receiving thy very welcome letter without writing to thee.

A late house surgeon of Joseph, now in practice in Glasgow, a warm approver of carbolic acid, told Joseph yesterday of a case he has treated—a terribly severe burn received by a poor boy in a foundry. We saw Dr. Watson (the doctor) the day that it had taken place, and he did not think that the boy *could* recover (so to speak) but by the help of carbolic acid he *is* recovering and the case has excited great interest in several foundries and deputations of their workmen have been sent to see the boy dressed and it is very probable that the boy's masters will appoint Dr. Watson surgeon to their works, which will give him a salary of £300 a year. Is it not very nice? There is a little girl in the Infirmary at present whose knee Joseph excised. She is about nine years old, I think. Yesterday she said to Joseph, "You might do the operation on the doll." Joseph asked what was wrong with the doll, and she said it had "a sair knee" and that the bran was coming out.

*　　　*　　　*　　　*　　　*

Lister had by this time applied his methods not only to cases of compound fracture and abscess but to all manner of surgical conditions. He was engaged also in the search for a better or simpler dressing than the lac plaster, when he received from Edinburgh the news which was destined to alter his career.

LISTER RETURNS TO EDINBURGH

Early in 1869 Professor Syme, whom he revered as teacher and as father-in-law, was smitten with paralysis and was obliged to relinquish the Chair of Clinical Surgery, and Lister was chosen as his successor. It must have been encouraging for him to receive a letter from 127 Edinburgh students, expressing their earnest wish that he should become a candidate. "We feel sure," they wrote, "that if you are appointed to this Chair, the benevolence of your character, and the urbanity of your manners, will speedily draw around you a large band of attached and devoted followers."

Those were prophetic words. Lister had been unsuccessful in his application for the Edinburgh Chair of Surgery when James Spence was

SIGNATURES OF SYME AND LISTER FROM A CASE-BOOK OF
EDINBURGH ROYAL INFIRMARY

appointed in 1864. He had failed also to secure the Chair at University College, London, in 1866, when the local candidate, John Marshall, was chosen to succeed Sir John Erichsen, and this had been a grievous disappointment to Lister, as he felt it might give him an opportunity of proclaiming his antiseptic gospel in London, where he would be surrounded by his family and friends. In the third attempt, however, he was fortunate, and his return to the previous field of work in Edinburgh was to prove peculiarly favourable to the scheme of research which he had envisaged. He had required little persuasion to apply for the Chair which James Syme had filled so ably. Lister was elected on 18th August 1869, and in October he and his wife were settled once again in Edinburgh.

E

CHAPTER VI

THE RETURN TO EDINBURGH

THE Listers lived in a furnished house at 17 Abercromby Place before purchasing the handsome residence in Edinburgh's most fashionable quarter, at 9 Charlotte Square, for which he paid what he called "a most enormous sum." One of the attractions of the new house was its proximity to Princes Street Gardens, a pleasure ground which was not then open to the public as it is to-day, but was reserved for the use of local residents, and in Lister's words was "a grand place to meditate in when I have it all to myself before breakfast." From 9 Charlotte Square, a house which still bears his name and the dates 1870-1877, he conducted a larger practice than at any other time of his career, he performed many of his experiments with micro-organisms before bacteriology became a science, and there, too, he and his wife entertained many friends and students and many distinguished visitors.

A Student visits Lister

One of these students, J. R. Leeson, who was Mayor of Twickenham at the time of his death in 1927, has recorded his first visit to Charlotte Square, in an interesting account of *Lister as I knew him* (1927).

"I felt instinctively that I was in the presence of a very unusual personality: such a combination of refinement, ability, benevolence, and sweetness of disposition as I had never before met; he seemed the embodiment of high purpose; an emanation of goodness radiated from him.

"I told him that the object of my visit was to bring Murchison's introduction and to ask if I might become one of his dressers. Reaching a little book from one of the drawers in his writing-table he entered my name, said I should begin next winter, and that meanwhile it would be well to familiarise myself with the work by attendance in his wards.

"He then led me to the windows before which on a long table were several rows of test-tubes covered with glass shades, half full of various liquids, and in the mouth of each was a plug of cotton wool.

"It was a curious assemblage such as I had never seen, nor could I form the least conjecture as to what they were or why they should be

66

plugged with cotton wool; my experience of test-tubes was an open mouth, and I never remember having seen them closed.

"With the greatest care and pride he picked out one here and there, held it up to the light and seemed inexplicably pleased at its condition: this was clear, this was turbid, and this was mouldy. Of course I tried to show an intelligent interest, but had not the faintest idea as to what it was all about and wondered what connection they could have with my visit or with any branch of surgery; and I remember thinking it strange that so eminent a surgeon should be interested in such an unusual subject and could find time to study such irrelevant and out-of-the-way matters."

*　　　*　　　*　　　*　　　*

"A kindly shake of the hand, another delightful and charming smile, and I found myself in the Square; its aspect seemed to have changed, it had lost much of its austerity, and I felt wildly glad that I had got through the visit and was now definitely on the road 'to dress for Lister'."

The Maid who swallowed a Pin

Another personal reminiscence of Lister, during his residence at Charlotte Square, is given by Miss Flora Masson in her *Victorians All*, 1931.

"Dr. Thomas Keith, tall and spare, with stooping shoulders, a sad face and a fair, pointed beard . . . was our kind and gentle family doctor. If Dr. Keith had been available—and I must have known that for some reason he was not—I should have no memory of the great Lister to record; for it would certainly have been Dr. Keith's address that I should have given to the cabman. As it was, the address I gave, on that memorable occasion, was No. 9 Charlotte Square.

"We ourselves, by that time, had moved into a house in Regent Terrace. Our parents were away for the day visiting friends across the Forth, and were not to be home till late in the evening. But the sun was still high in the heavens when the great catastrophe occurred. One of the maids announced the fact that she had swallowed a pin. Trembling, and in tears, she managed to say, between little spasmodic gulps, that it was a bent pin, and that it was sticking in her throat, not very far down.

"I suppose I fancied myself in charge; at any rate I assumed an authority which seems to have been accorded. I sent for a cab, and the maid and I got into it. I still wonder at my audacity in driving to Professor Lister's house in Charlotte Square.

"We were shown into the dining-room, and immediately, while we were still standing, the great surgeon came in. He stood, silently benign, looking at us, while I made my little explanatory appeal. I had prepared it, in my own mind, as we were driving in the cab. Our maid had said she had swallowed a pin, a bent pin—and she felt it sticking in her throat—not very far down; and my father and mother (I am afraid I said papa and mamma; people did in those days) were away for the day, and I did not quite know what I ought to do, to whom I ought to come; but they would be back that evening, and I was sure they would call on him themselves —to thank him—the very next day.

"I remember the kind, grave face looking down at me as he listened; and without a word he led the way into his consulting-room. I remember the look of the chair, a glorified dentist's chair, in which he placed the trembling girl. I remember standing by—indeed, she had taken a firm grip of me—and watching the surgeon's hands, their leisurely, gentle manipulation of the long, shining instruments; they seemed to grow longer and longer as the search for that pin proceeded.

"Then, at last, he desisted. 'I do not think,' he said slowly, looking at the girl in the chair, 'there is any pin there. I think, if there had been, I should have found it.'

"He came with us out into the hall, the girl drying her eyes. At the open door—the cab waiting to take us back—he shook hands.

"'You may tell Professor and Mrs. Masson,' he said, smiling benignly, 'that I don't think there is any pin there. You may say, if there had been, I think I should have found it.'

"That is my childhood memory of the great surgeon."

DEATHS OF SYME AND SIMPSON

It may be of interest to recall the characterisation of some of the distinguished men who were Lister's colleagues during his second term of residence in Edinburgh. Two of the leaders, Syme and Simpson, were approaching the end of their brilliant careers. Syme rallied for a few months after his retirement in 1869, but a further paralytic stroke led to his death on 26th June 1870. He had been a man of strong opinions, who did not deal gently with those who opposed him. Nevertheless "the hostility which he excited in a few was greatly outweighed by the friendship he inspired in the many. Besides being a surgical genius of the highest order, Mr. Syme was a perfect gentleman, and a good as well as a great man." Those words form part of the obituary notice of Syme in the *Scotsman*, unsigned but said to have been written by Lister. To Syme, Lister owed much, and he would remark very often to his students, "Ah, gentlemen, one of the many things I learned from Mr. Syme."

Simpson, to whom reference has already been made, continued to lead a life of intense activity in spite of severe attacks of angina pectoris. He died at the age of fifty-eight, two months before Syme, with whom he had been frequently in conflict. A man of great versatility, his incursion into the field of surgery and his introduction of "acupressure" had been strongly resented by Syme, and he had rendered Lister's work more difficult by his opposition to the antiseptic principle and by his scepticism regarding the results.

Of the three men, a former student, H. A. Lediard of Carlisle, has written in a letter of personal reminiscences: "Syme was irritable and domineering, but we would have fought for him to the last. Simpson was venomous and sarcastic, and enjoyed a bitter controversy. Lister was patience and sympathy personified."

There was still another death, at the time of Lister's return to Edinburgh, which had its influence on his career. Lister's father, who had watched and guided with such wise and loving care each step of his son's victorious path, was no longer to be available as mentor and counsellor. He died in September, 1869, at the age of eighty-four. Lister's mother had died in 1864 after a long illness, so that now the old family home at Upton was to be broken up, and the old associations were to end.

The Unhealthy Surgical Wards

Another misfortune tended to cloud the happiness of Lister just after his return to Edinburgh. This was a controversy in *The Lancet* and the *Glasgow Herald* regarding certain statements published by Lister in the former journal in January, 1870. The article was entitled "On the Effects of the Antiseptic System on the Salubrity of a Surgical Hospital." Lister pointed out that the good results of his antiseptic system could not be attributed to improved environment, whether in ventilation, diet or nursing, as no improvement had been made at the time of his discovery. His remarkable results had been obtained in wards which were "the most unhealthy in the kingdom." The Managers of the Glasgow Royal Infirmary resented such a description of their new hospital, but of course Lister had never intended to make such an accusation (Plate XIV). All that he wished was to show that his success was entirely due to the antiseptic principle, and that in the peculiarly unhealthy wards of a very large hospital, a degree of salubrity equal to that of the best private houses had been attained. In a dignified reply to the attack, he wrote that "to suppose that the kind of change which I have described as having taken place in the salubrity of my wards can be attributed to the causes referred to, is simply out of the question. As regards the ventilation of those wards, it remains precisely as it was, with the exception of a freer access of air to the back of the hospital, in consequence of taking down the high wall, as mentioned in my paper; and this was not done till my patients had been already for nine months perfectly free from hospital diseases. As to nursing, my department was not affected by the change that occurred. I was fortunate enough to have excellent nurses from the commencement of my connection with the infirmary, and I continued to have such to the last. And as to dietary, the idea that a mere improvement in rations would abolish pyæmia, erysipelas and hospital gangrene, is one which would hardly enter the mind of an intelligent medical man."

Fortunately Lister's successor in Glasgow, Mr. Macleod (later Sir George Macleod), was a supporter of the antiseptic doctrine, and the controversy soon died down.

LISTER'S EDINBURGH COLLEAGUES

Let us return, however, to the colleagues who were to share with Lister the credit of bringing fame to the Edinburgh Medical School. Perhaps the most prominent was the veteran Sir Robert Christison, Professor of Materia Medica, who previously had been Professor of Medical Jurisprudence. He had studied under Orfila, the greatest toxicologist of Paris, and had written a noteworthy *Treatise on Poisons*. His services were in demand as a consulting physician, although he was essentially a university man, and had determined, early in his career, "to make the Chair his primary object and let physician's practice look after itself." Gifted with a fine voice and a ready wit, he was a popular figure at public gatherings, an honour shared by his successor in the Chair of Medical Jurisprudence, Sir Douglas Maclagan, then plain Dr. Maclagan, whose songs, with a topical and medical flavour, were highly popular, and were published under the title *Nugæ Canoræ Medicæ*. Although Christison was over seventy years of age when Lister became Professor in Edinburgh, he was still very active in mind and body. He climbed Edinburgh's mountain, Arthur's Seat, in nine minutes in 1825 (aged 29), in fifteen minutes in 1855 (age 59), and in twenty-two minutes in 1875 (age 78). In 1879, when he was 82 years of age, he ascended Ben Vrackie, near Pitlochry, which was no mean feat.

Other University Chairs were held by men hardly less distinguished. Greek, and much else besides, was taught by John Stuart Blackie, Geology by Sir Archibald Geikie, while Crum Brown had just been appointed Professor of Chemistry. Each was a giant in his own sphere of work.

Hughes Bennett, who popularised the medicinal use of cod-liver oil, was Professor of Physiology, or the Institutes of Medicine, as it was still called.

The Professor of Medicine was an Englishman, Thomas Laycock, an able neurologist who was one of the first to teach medical psychology.

The physician who probably had the largest consulting practice of the time was the popular and kindly James Warburton Begbie, a near neighbour of Lister in Charlotte Square. A man of wide interests, Begbie gave several courses of lectures on the History of Medicine.

The Chair of Anatomy had passed from the third member of the Monro dynasty to John Goodsir, and then, in 1867, to William Turner, who later became Sir William Turner and Principal of the University. Turner was an Englishman, a fact which probably cemented his lifelong friendship with Lister.

Another close friend of Lister was Matthews Duncan, who, like his colleague Thomas Keith, was a pioneer of gynæcology and an assistant of Sir James Y. Simpson. Both of these men had been present on the historic occasion, and had actually been subjects of the experiment when Simpson in 1847 discovered the anæsthetic properties of chloroform, in the dining-room of his house at 52 Queen Street. Matthews Duncan failed to secure the Chair of Obstetrics after the death of Simpson, but he removed to London in 1877 and attained distinction there. Keith followed him a few years later.

An important step had been taken in 1862 by the appointment of the first Medical Officer of Health for Edinburgh in the person of Henry Littlejohn. Dr. Littlejohn, who became Sir Henry Littlejohn, was distinguished not only in Public Health but also in Medical Jurisprudence. He eventually succeeded Sir Douglas Maclagan as professor of the latter subject, and his dramatic style of lecturing produced a deep impression on all his students.

THE CHAIRS OF SYSTEMATIC AND CLINICAL SURGERY

In the field of surgery there was James Spence, who had been appointed to the Chair when Lister was an unsuccessful candidate in 1864.

"Dismal Jamie," as he was called, was of morose type, but he was a stoic nevertheless, and when he had the misfortune to have his leg amputated in later life he showed a scientific interest in the result. "Give me my foot and my box of scalpels," he said, as soon as he had sufficiently recovered from the operation, "I want to dissect out the tendon sheaths."

Another surgeon was Patrick Heron Watson (later Sir Patrick), an associate of Lister's in the days when he was Syme's house-surgeon. He had served in the Crimea, and was now conducting a large practice, being one of the last of the Edinburgh surgeons who also practised as a physician. Amongst the juniors was Thomas Annandale, who had assisted Syme, and who later succeeded Lister in the Edinburgh Chair of Clinical Surgery. There was also John Duncan, an able surgeon and a popular teacher.

Two other junior surgeons of the time who became famous were John Chiene and Joseph Bell. John Chiene, who had been house-surgeon to Syme, became one of Lister's most enthusiastic supporters. Later, he succeeded Spence in the Chair of Systematic Surgery, and became one of the best teachers of surgery which Edinburgh had known. Throughout their lives, those who had been his pupils could recall the pithy sayings of this master of epigram.

Joseph Bell was another able surgeon and a good teacher, the first Surgeon to the Royal Hospital for Sick Children. He came of a surgical family, and was the great-grandson of Benjamin Bell, who was the first in Edinburgh to confine his practice to surgery and who was the author of a popular text-book. "Joe" Bell had a fondness for noting the characteristics of the patients who consulted him, and one of his students, Conan Doyle, made use of those methods in delineating the well-known detective of fiction, Sherlock Holmes.

This, then, was the environment into which Joseph Lister stepped as, at the age of forty-two, he passed from the Chair of Glasgow to that of Edinburgh, and those were some of his associates during his tenure of office.

THE OLD INFIRMARY

The Clinical Surgery lectures were held only twice a week, which must have been a relief to Lister after his years of daily lectures on Systematic Surgery in Glasgow. The scene of Lister's work as Professor was the building in High School Yards which, after the present Royal Infirmary was opened in 1879 on the site facing the open ground of "The Meadows," came to be known as "The Old Infirmary" (Plate XV). How vividly Henley describes his own experience as a patient: he had already lost a

PLATE XV

THE SURGICAL BLOCK OF THE OLD ROYAL INFIRMARY OF EDINBURGH, FORMERLY THE ROYAL HIGH SCHOOL, AND NOW THE GEOGRAPHY DEPARTMENT OF THE UNIVERSITY. LISTER'S WARDS WERE ON THE GROUND FLOOR

Facing page 72

PLATE XVI

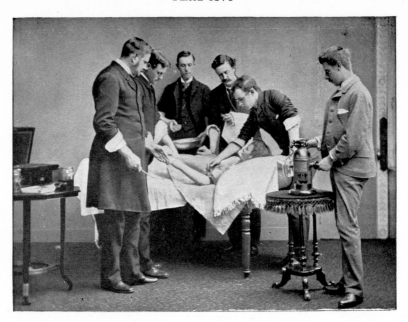

AN OPERATION AT ABERDEEN, ABOUT 1880. THE FOURTH FIGURE FROM THE LEFT IS SIR ALEXANDER OGSTON. ALL CONCERNED ARE WEARING THEIR ORDINARY CLOTHES, INCLUDING THE OPERATOR AND THE ASSISTANT WHO MANIPULATES THE SPRAY. THE ERA OF GOWNS, CAPS, MASKS AND GLOVES HAD NOT YET ARRIVED

THE STEAM SPRAY AS USED BY LISTER

foot from tuberculosis, and the other was saved from amputation by
Lister's treatment:—

Enter Patient

The morning mists still haunt the stony street;
  The northern summer air is shrill and cold:
  And lo, the Hospital, grey, quiet, old,
Where Life and Death like friendly chafferers meet.

*   *   *   *

The grey-haired soldier-porter waves me on,
And on I crawl, and still my spirits fail:
  A tragic meanness seems so to environ
  These corridors and stairs of stone and iron,
Cold, naked, clean—half-workhouse and half-jail.

These corridors, he might have added, had their own peculiar smell,
a sort of mixture of stale tobacco smoke, carbolic acid, and boiled beef.
The surgical wards previously had been part of the High School, and were
ill-adapted to the purposes of a hospital. There, fifty beds were allotted to
Lister's charge, and there he taught, as so vividly described by Lister's
nephew, Sir Rickman Godlee, who writes in his *Lord Lister*:—

"The capacious operating-theatre, seated for four or five hundred,
such as may still be seen in America, but seldom now in this country,
was packed up to the top row. There was a large 'area,' or ground
space, surrounded by chairs for a dozen or more distinguished visitors,
which were often all occupied. Four dressers, in blue check aprons,
brought in the patient on a long wicker basket, and placed him on the
table. The notes were read by the clerk, and the Professor proceeded
to discourse in deliberate and clear language, without show or orna-
ment, but rendered piquant by a very slight stammer and an occasional
flash of quiet humour. The special feature of Lister's lectures was
that they did not consist so much in a description of the particular
pathological condition from which the patient was suffering, or the
clinical details of diagnosis or treatment, as in eliciting from each case
some fundamental lesson of far-reaching application. He was therefore not at great pains to seek out examples of obscure disease. An
ulcer of the leg, an old dislocation, a chronic abscess, served his purpose equally well, or even better. The lectures gave what no book
could supply, and for this reason were never tedious, but held the
close attention of the students. And though some might regret that
so many paths led up at last inevitably to the antiseptic doctrine, it

was found, by the end of the session, that a large part of the surgical field had been gone over in travelling there. In the course of a single lecture perhaps three or four patients were brought into the theatre; and sometimes, but not always, an operation was performed upon the last, which gave the opportunity of explaining the principles underlying the mechanical art of surgery."

The poet, W. E. Henley, a patient in 1873, records as follows his impressions of Lister in the oft-quoted lines, entitled "The Chief":—

"His brow spreads large and placid, and his eye
Is deep and bright, with steady looks that still.
Soft lines of tranquil thought his face fulfill—
His face at once benign and proud and shy.
If envy scout, if ignorance deny,
His faultless patience, his unyielding will,
Beautiful gentleness, and splendid skill,
Innumerable gratitudes reply.
His wise, rare smile is sweet with certainties,
And seems in all his patients to compel
Such love and faith as failure cannot quell.
We hold him for another Herakles,
Battling with custom, prejudice, disease.
As once the son of Zeus with Death and Hell."

Lister's devotion to his work and his unfailing courtesy to his patients caused all who met him to revere him. To Lister the hospital was a temple, and he could not endure any infringement of its sanctity. On one occasion he had performed a brilliant operation in thirty-two seconds, and when the onlookers cheered him he turned and remarked, "Gentlemen, gentlemen, remember where you are." To students and patients he was a hero, whom they idolised. Yet there were critics among his colleagues who either misused his methods or frankly disapproved of them.

MISUNDERSTANDINGS

Before Lister assumed the duties of the Chair of Clinical Surgery at Edinburgh, the antiseptic principle had been fairly launched, but much opposition was encountered before it met with general acceptance. Some of the early misunderstandings have already been mentioned. Those who spoke of the new treatment as "the carbolic method" could not hope to secure results comparable to those of Lister. Even Sir James Paget, the distinguished London surgeon whose *Memoir and Letters* give such a vivid picture of the surgical practice of his time, imagined that he was following Lister's method in treating a compound fracture of the leg by sealing the wound with collodion, and applying carbolic acid twelve hours later. Lister felt bound to point out to him that those two substances act upon totally different principles, "the former mechanically excluding the air with its floating organisms, whilst the latter operated upon the putrefactive germs as a poison. . . . To combine collodion and carbolic acid is to do not only what I never thought of recommending, but what I should regard as objectionable, since the former would tend to obstruct the free exit of the sero-sanguineous effusion which the stimulating action of the latter would promote." Other surgeons spoke disparagingly of Lister's method without even having tried it. The treatment demanded careful study and the adoption of a new technique, and few of Lister's contemporaries were willing to take the trouble to alter the well-worn rules. Strangely enough, his views were accepted more readily on the Continent than in Britain, and more than one of his students has recorded how frequently he was wont to remark, "Well, gentlemen, it is no new thing for me to be misunderstood."

Those who associated Lister simply with carbolic acid as a new discovery were bound to fail: "from the statements of some, you would suppose me to have taught that, if you do but apply carbolic acid freely to a wound you will prevent suppuration; whereas I have all along pointed out that carbolic acid, being a stimulating substance, will itself induce suppuration by long-continued action on the tissues."

ENCOURAGEMENT FROM DENMARK

Only those who had really studied his technique, and who knew the principle on which it was based, could hope to secure successful results. One of those was Professor Saxtorph of Copenhagen, who had paid a long visit to Lister in Glasgow. "Well do I remember that my old friend Professor Saxtorph was the first of Continental surgeons to adopt the antiseptic system!" So wrote Lister to Professor Salomonsen of Copenhagen, in 1902. The letter is preserved in the Medico-Historical Museum of Copenhagen, and beside it is another, to Dr. F. C. C. Hansen, in which Lister again refers to the fact that "my honoured friend Professor Saxtorph of your University was the first to apply the antiseptic principle in a Continental hospital."

In July, 1870, Saxtorph wrote to Lister, then in Edinburgh, and reported remarkable results. "The Frederik's Hospital, to which I am head surgeon," he explained, "is a very old building, and I have 150 patients in the surgical wards. Formerly there used to be every year several cases of death from pyæmia, sometimes arising from the most trivial injuries. Now, I have had the satisfaction that not a single case of pyæmia has occurred since I came home last year, which result is certainly owing to the introduction of your antiseptic treatment. But it must be clear to any surgeon who has adopted your method that unless you take the greatest precautions in every dressing until the wound is healed, you will never see the excellent effects of this treatment."

Such a letter, coming from one who had given his method a fair and thorough trial, brought great encouragement to Lister, although he was completely free from vanity, and fully realised that he must still fight on for years before his discovery could be universally understood and appreciated. Years later, in 1902, on receiving the Copley Medal of the Royal Society, he said that "he had often thought that if he did deserve any credit at all it was at a time when, perfectly convinced of the truth of the principle on which he acted, and persuaded of the enormous importance to mankind of being able to carry out that principle in practice, he worked for years together with exceedingly little encouragement from his professional brethren. There were two great exceptions, however, his father-in-law and his students."

His father-in-law, the great Syme, was now gone, and he must plough a lone furrow. There were, nevertheless, a few enthusiastic supporters during the Edinburgh period; among the juniors, John Chiene and John Duncan, who have been mentioned, as well as Hector Cameron of Glasgow and Alexander Ogston of Aberdeen, both of whom grasped the principle from the first. Bickersteth of Liverpool, Lund of Manchester, and Cadge of Norwich were among the English supporters of Lister, but for the most part surgeons were either apathetic and indifferent, or actually antagonistic.

Lister himself was not content with his achievement, great though it had been. That there was room for improvement he knew very well, and it was at the time of his return to Edinburgh that he introduced two important innovations, the gauze dressing and the spray. He was far from satisfied with the non-absorbent lac plaster as a wound dressing, and he sought carefully for a substitute.

New Dressings

At first the teased-out tarry hempen rope known as oakum, soaked in carbolic acid solution, was tried, but it was sticky and unpleasant. A further long search among the wares of drapers' establishments brought to Lister's notice a muslin gauze which was soft, absorbent, and fairly cheap.

Many experiments were necessary in order to discover how the gauze could be impregnated with the antiseptic, but at last this was found possible by combining it with resin. This carbolised gauze, pale yellow in colour, was applied as a pad eight layers thick, and between the seventh and eighth layer there was introduced a layer of waterproof material, known in the trade as "hat lining," or "jaconet," stained pink so that its position in the dressing might be obvious, and so that seven superimposed layers of gauze might be next to the wound. The mackintosh or waterproof served the purpose of forcing the discharge to travel to the edge of the dressing instead of soaking straight through.

The gauze dressing was retained in position by a gauze bandage, fixed here and there with safety pins, and it remained a favourite application to wounds for some years—in fact until Lister introduced, first, a gauze containing corrosive sublimate, called sal alembroth gauze, and next, a gauze permeated with the double cyanide of mercury and zinc, and stained heliotrope to distinguish it. This, in turn, has now been replaced by sterile gauze, but the fact remains, a fact often forgotten, that it was Lister who introduced into surgery the absorbent gauze dressing and the gauze "swabs" now so familiar to every one.

Reference will be made in a later chapter of this book (page 103) to the replacement of the antiseptic by the aseptic technique, although Lister's principle remained unaltered. Lister was fully aware of the disadvantage of using an antiseptic, and was constantly searching for some milder substance which might replace carbolic acid and be less harmful to the tissues. Mercuric chloride, or corrosive sublimate, as it was called, seemed to provide a suitable dressing, but it did not penetrate grease and it corroded instruments. Therefore carbolic acid remained in use.

Nevertheless this search for a milder application led to the introduction of boracic acid as an antiseptic. Lister found that lint could be saturated with this substance, and thus he introduced boracic lint, another of his many discoveries, and one which is often forgotten. It was only at a later stage that it was found to possess a feeble antiseptic power, but it remains in use as a favourite form of dressing.

THE HISTORY OF THE SPRAY

The second improvement in Lister's technical equipment was the spray, first described by Lister in his Address to the British Medical

Association at Plymouth in 1871. He was convinced that the germs which gained admission to wounds with such disastrous effects were airborne, and this conviction was strengthened by the experiments of the well-known physicist John Tyndall, whose popular lectures familiarised his hearers with the "germ theory," and showed them how floating dust might contain myriads of germs. His demonstration of the dust in a beam of light and of the effect of this dust in causing putrefaction were sufficient to convince the most sceptical member of his audience.

Lister was well aware of the part played by the air as a medium for germs, and it was natural that he should wish to plan his technique so as to prevent the germs from reaching the wound by this route.

Thus arose the spray, an attempt to create an antiseptic atmosphere in which operations and dressings could be conducted. At first an ordinary rubber bulb spray was used, called Richardson's spray, and already in use for local anæsthesia. The carbolic acid solution used in the spray consisted of one part of carbolic acid to a hundred parts of water, and it was disseminated by the spray as a cloud of vapour in which all the surgical manipulations were conducted. It was hard work to keep the spray going, but however much his hand ached, not one of the student "dressers" would ever give in, although, on occasion, one of them would faint from the continued effort. One of Lister's house-surgeons, Watson Cheyne, later the distinguished London surgeon Sir Watson Cheyne, has described how the dresser would pump furiously with the spray while Lister removed the dressing, and then the protective oil silk, and show the healthy wound to the surprised foreigners who so often formed his audience. "Violent conversation would break out among them accompanied by equally violent gesticulations." They recognised that here was something unparalleled in the history of surgery. The spray underwent a steady evolution, the second stage being that of a large spray, mounted on a tripod, and manipulated by a long pump handle. A cumbrous machine, it could not be easily concealed, and part of it projected from the window of Lister's brougham as he drove to visit his patients. From its appearance, it was called "the donkey engine," but it soon gave place to the steam spray, which was used for many years by Lister and by his disciples in various parts of the world (Plate XVI). It entailed little effort on the part of the dresser, and produced a large cloud of vapour, although it had many disadvantages, not the least of which was the effect of the carbolic acid solution, which had now been strengthened to one in forty instead of one in a hundred of water, upon the hands of the operator and his assistants. Indeed the rough "carbolic hand" of the surgeon was often a matter of

78

comment. Mr. W. J. Stuart, Consulting Surgeon to Edinburgh Royal Infirmary, has kindly permitted the author to include the following remarks from a recent letter: "When I began surgical work in 1894 in the wards of John Duncan, my uncle, the towels were wrung out of 1 in 20 carbolic and were kept in a large glass jar. John Duncan took off his frock coat, but nothing else, and only very occasionally had a dry towel pinned round his neck, as you describe Lister. How well do I remember our hands when we were instrument clerks at that time, the instruments being in 1 in 20, and one's hand soaked in it for a whole morning. One's fingers were absolutely white from the carbolic by the end of the morning."

There were no rubber gloves in those days, nor were there masks, or even overalls, and few surgeons even troubled to remove their jackets, or rather their "frock coats," such being the recognised fashion for the professional man. Accordingly both patient and surgeon were obliged to inhale some carbolic vapour, and there were many cases of carbolic acid poisoning, though for the most part mild, in the days of the spray.

The spray remained in use by Lister until 1887. He recognised its disadvantages, but could not feel justified in discarding it, although various surgeons had suggested a return to irrigation, including Bruns of Tübingen, who wrote a vigorous article entitled "Fort mit dem Spray" (Away with the Spray). Gradually, however, he came to realise that the fingers, the instruments, and the dressings and sponges and the skin of the patient were much more potent as carriers of germs than was the air. At the time of which we write, however, the spray was an essential part of the ritual. "Spray, please," Lister would say, and the familiar hiss of the apparatus with its cloud of moisture would announce that the "clerk" or "dresser" in charge of this important adjunct had turned on the tap.

Duties of equal importance were allotted to the instrument clerk. He was responsible for the sponges, which had not then given place to gauze swabs, and for the instruments which, in deference to the feelings of the patient, were always kept covered until actually required.

ATTENTION TO DETAIL

Lister was most careful and thorough in everything he did, and he never tired of telling his students that "Success depends upon attention to detail." Even so small an accessory as the safety pin was of importance to him. He preferred black safety pins, which were easily seen, and he taught that they should be placed parallel to the line of strain and not across it, so that they might not buckle or tear the bandage. He carried out all his own dressings during his ward round, and before leaving each patient he would ask, "Now, are you quite comfortable?" and would adjust the pillows with his own hands. A favourite aphorism was often quoted: "There is one rule in surgery. Put yourself in the patient's place," although Lister never referred to patients as "the case," but always as "this good woman" or "this poor man." In the administration of chloroform he was an expert. He preferred it to ether, and he had it administered, by the clerk set apart for this duty, on a folded towel, but with plenty of room for air, after the approved method of the Edinburgh school. "Watch the breathing carefully, and never go on with the anæsthetic unless the patient is breathing naturally."

It was shortly after his return to Edinburgh that he was summoned to Balmoral Castle to attend Queen Victoria, who was suffering from an abscess of the axilla. The abscess was opened by Lister, while Sir William Jenner, her Majesty's physician, worked the spray, and later the Queen congratulated Lister upon "a most disagreeable duty most agreeably performed."

On this occasion he observed that the strip of lint which he was accustomed to use as a drain might really act as a plug, and actually hinder drainage. He therefore cut off a piece of rubber tubing from the spray, cut side holes in it and thus improvised a drainage tube, the first occasion on which he used one, as he was unaware that the French surgeon Chassaignac had anticipated him in this discovery.

LISTER'S VIEWS ON ANIMAL EXPERIMENTS

The association with Queen Victoria had a curious sequel. A few years later a Royal Commission was appointed to enquire into the practice of so-called vivisection, and the Queen, "dreadfully shocked" at "unnecessary and horrible cruelties," appealed to Lister to make a public declaration against the practice. This, of course, he could not do. Although he was the most humane of men, he had found it necessary for the purposes of his researches to perform operations upon animals under anæsthesia. In a carefully worded reply to the Queen he explained that such experiments were carried out in order to lessen human misery and suffering, and that more pain was inflicted upon the hunted stag or hare, or upon animals fattened for human food, than upon any animal in a laboratory. "It might," he concluded, "be safely left to the humane feelings of those members of the medical profession whom an ardent desire for the pursuit of truth and the benefit of their fellow creatures may urge to prosecute such investigations," and that "legislation on this subject is wholly uncalled for." Nevertheless his letter did not cause her Majesty to alter her opinion, nor did his evidence before the Royal Commission prevent the introduction of the Cruelty to Animals Act, which became law in 1876.

Lister's views regarding experiments on animals were clearly expressed in a letter to Professor W. W. Keen of Philadelphia, dated 1898. A Bill had been introduced into Congress with a view to prohibiting animal experimentation, and it was strongly opposed by many leaders of the medical profession. William W. Keen, Professor of Surgery at Jefferson Medical College, Philadelphia, a pioneer of brain surgery and a foremost surgeon of the day, wrote to Lord Lister requesting his support in opposing the Bill. Lister's reply gave such an explicit and reasoned opinion that it assisted the eventual rejection of the Bill, and the letter is worth reading, even at the present day, as his contribution to a problem which still exists.

> 12 PARK CRESCENT,
> PORTLAND PLACE,
> LONDON, W.
> *4th April* 1898.

MY DEAR SIR,

I am grieved to learn that there should be even a remote chance of the Legislature of any State in the Union passing a bill for regulating experiments upon animals.

It is only comparatively recently in the World's history that the gross darkness of empiricism has given place to more and more scientific practice; and this result has been mainly due to experiments upon living animals. It was to these that Harvey was in large measure indebted for the fundamental discovery of the circulation of the blood, and the great American triumph of general anæsthesia was greatly promoted by them. Advancing knowledge has shewn more and more that the bodies of the lower animals are essentially similar to our own in their intimate structure and functions: so that lessons learned from them may be applied to human pathology and treatment. If we refuse to avail ourselves of this means of acquiring increased acquaintance with the working of that marvellously complex machine, the animal body, we must either be content to remain at an absolute stand-still or return to the fearful haphazard ways of testing new remedies upon human patients in the first instance which prevailed in the dark ages.

Never was there a time when the advantages that may accrue to man from investigations in the lower animals were more conspicuous than now. The enormous advances that have been made in our knowledge of the nature and treatment of disease of late years have been essentially due to work of this kind. The importance of such investigations was fully recognised by the Commissioners on whose report the Act of Parliament regulating experiments on animals in this country was passed, their object in recommending legislation being professedly only to prevent possible abuse. In reality, as one of the Commissioners, the late Mr. Erichsen, informed me, no single instance of such abuse having occurred in the British Islands had been brought before them at the time when I gave my evidence, and that was towards the close of their sittings. Yet in obedience to a popular outcry, the Government of the day passed an Act which went much further than the recommendations of the Commissioners. They had advised that the operation of the law should be restricted to experiments upon warm-blooded animals; but when the bill was considered in the House of Commons a Member who was greatly respected as a Politician but entirely ignorant of the subject matter suggested that "vertebrated" should be substituted for "warm-blooded," and this amendment was accepted by a majority as ignorant as himself.

The result is that, incredible as it may seem, anyone would now be liable to criminal prosecution in this country who should observe the circulation of the blood in a frog's foot under the microscope without having obtained a licence for the experiment and unless he performed it in a specially licensed place.

It can be readily understood that such restrictions must seriously interfere with legitimate researches. Indeed for the private practitioner they are almost prohibitive, and no one can tell how much valuable work is thus prevented.

My own first investigations of any importance were a study of the process of inflammation in the transparent web of the frog's foot. The experiments were very numerous and were performed at all hours of the day in my own house. I was then a young unknown practitioner; and if the present law had been in existence, it might have been difficult for me to obtain the requisite licences; and even if I had got them, it would have been impossible for me to have gone to a public laboratory to work. Yet without these early researches, which the existing law would have prevented, I could not have found my way among the perplexing difficulties which beset me in developing the antiseptic system of treatment in Surgery.

In the course of my antiseptic work at a later period I frequently had recourse to experiments on animals. One of these occurs to me which yielded particularly valuable results, but which I certainly should not have done if the present law had been in force. It had reference to the behaviour of a thread composed of animal tissue applied antiseptically for tying an arterial trunk. I had prepared a ligature of such material at a house where I was spending a few days at a distance from home; and it occurred to me to test it upon the carotid artery of a calf. Acting on the spur of the moment, I procured the needful animal at a neighbouring market; a lay friend gave chloroform and another assisted at the operation. Four weeks later the calf was killed and its neck was sent to me. On my dissecting it, the beautiful truth was revealed that the dead material of the thread, instead of being thrown off by suppuration, had been replaced under the new aseptic conditions, by a firm ring of living fibrous tissue, the old dangers of such an operation being completely obviated.

I have referred thus to my personal experience because requested to do so; and these examples are perhaps sufficient to illustrate the impediments which the existing law places in the way of research by medical men engaged in practice, whose ideas, if developed, would often be the most fruitful in beneficent results.

But even those who are specialists in physiology or pathology, and have ready access to research laboratories, find their work very seriously hampered by the necessity of applying for licences for all investigations and the difficulty and delay often encountered in obtaining them. Our law on this subject should never have been passed and ought to be repealed. It serves no good purpose and interferes seriously with enquiries which are of paramount importance to mankind.

Believe me
Sincerely yours,
LISTER.

Professor Keen.

LISTER AS BACTERIOLOGIST

During his tenure of the Edinburgh Chair, Lister devoted much attention to a study of the nature and life history of those "germs" which his antiseptic method was designed to antagonise. Lister's service to surgery is now universally recognised, as also is his contribution to physiology, but his work as a pioneer of bacteriology is apt to be forgotten. The problem which confronted him was indeed profound. Little was known of the "germs" of disease, and their very existence was not accepted by all scientists. Pasteur had founded a new science by demonstrating that fermentation was caused by living organisms and was not merely a chemical process, but this knowledge was as yet nebulous, and it had not been proved. It was not until Robert Koch had published, in 1876, his methods of fixing and staining bacteria (as the "germs" came to be called), and not until, in 1881, when Koch had shown how they might be isolated and grown on solid media, that a real advance was made.

Only then did it become recognised that each infective disease was the product of its own particular organism.

Thereafter, until the end of the century, announcements of the discoveries of new bacilli followed each other in rapid succession. Pasteur, (born 1822), Lister (born 1827), and Koch (born 1843) were the three pioneers of bacteriology, which thus had its roots in France, Britain and Germany.

Lister, when he began his researches, was entering an uncharted sea.

83

He was obliged to devise his own technique and this he did with great enthusiasm. In a letter to his brother Arthur, who was an authority on fungi, he wrote in February, 1872: "I have been labouring hard, I may say, at the subject of these wee organisms, and have made some progress"; and in another letter, three weeks later, "I am terribly busy snatching time whenever I can get it for work at the organisms. But though I never work at the subject without getting some new and interesting fact, yet when it is all put together the sum of my product seems a very insignificant affair."

Lister chose the yeast "plant," Torula cerevisiæ, as his first subject of study, and in a paper to the Royal Society of Edinburgh in 1875 he showed how organisms vary according to their environment, how a "torula" may arise from a filamentous fungus. The illustrations to this article are a commentary on Lister's zeal. Not only days but nights were devoted to the investigation, as is shown by the note of the hour of observation appended to each drawing, to illustrate the appearance of the organism and its varying shapes. The drawings are timed, 12th September 1872, not only at 1.30 a.m., 6 a.m., 10.45 a.m., and 5.30 p.m., but also 3.30 a.m. on 13th September. Some of his conclusions were incorrect, but they are none the less surprising when we remember that his apparatus was merely a series of test-tubes under a glass cover, originally sterilised by what he called a "hot box," the forerunner of the steam steriliser. One important fact which he proved was that the growth of organisms was not always productive of an odour, as had been imagined. Lister, as he dressed the patients in his ward, would often hand round the dressing so that his audience might satisfy themselves by the sense of smell that there was no "putrefaction." But now he discovered that an albuminous fluid might ferment without producing any odour, and thus he showed that the term "putrefaction" must be altered, when applied in the surgical sense, to the more correct term "infection." The extent of Lister's long and painstaking investigations is obvious from his careful and extensive notes, many of which are contained in the four folio volumes preserved in the library of the Royal College of Surgeons of England.

Correspondence with Pasteur

It was during the course of those investigations that Lister wrote his first letter to Pasteur. The letter, dated 13th February 1874, contains the following sentences:—

"I do not know whether the records of British Surgery ever meet your eye. If so, you will have seen from time to time notices of the

THE RETURN TO EDINBURGH

antiseptic system of treatment, which I have been labouring for the last nine years to bring to perfection. Allow me to take this opportunity to tender you my most cordial thanks for having, by your brilliant researches, demonstrated to me the truth of the germ theory of putrefaction, and thus furnished me with the principle upon which alone the antiseptic system can be carried out."

Pasteur replied with great cordiality, remarking that "it is an enigma to me that you can devote yourself to researches which demand so much care, time, and incessant painstaking, at the same time as you devote yourself to the profession of surgery and to that of chief surgeon to a great hospital."

The Antiseptic Method in Germany

As has been already remarked, the discovery of Lister was accepted on the Continent while it made little headway at home. Especially in Germany was the new method adopted with enthusiasm, notably by Thiersch of Leipzig and by Volkmann of Halle. The latter returned from the Franco-Prussian War in 1872 to find his wards crowded with soldiers suffering from severely infected wounds. He thought of closing the hospital, but decided to give Lister's methods a trial. The result was magical. Pyæmia was banished and the death rate fell dramatically. Richard Volkmann became Lister's faithful pupil (*treuester Junger*) and his champion in spreading the antiseptic doctrine. Another German colleague, Stromeyer of Hanover, commemorated the occasion in light verse, and even wrote an English translation:

Lister

Mankind looks gratefull now on Thee
For what Thou didst in Surgery.
And Death must often go amiss,
By smelling antiseptik bliss.

By Volkmann's skill and industry
Famous Thou art in Germany!
Who could a better Prophet be,
Than Richard Hotspur was to Thee?

Nussbaum of Munich had an experience very similar to that of Volkmann. At his hospital, pyæmia and gangrene were so prevalent in 1872 that 80 per cent. of all wounds were affected, and the death rate was

85

terrifying. The antiseptic method was adopted, and "in the course of a single week . . . we experienced one surprise after another." Everything went well. "Not another case of hospital gangrene appeared . . . our results became better and better, the time of healing shorter, and the pyæmia and erysipelas completely disappeared." In 1875 Nussbaum wrote a little book on the antiseptic treatment of wounds (*Leitfaden zur antiseptischen Wundebehandlung*), which was translated into French, Italian and Greek, and which did much to spread the gospel of antisepsis. To Lister he wrote: "I hold that next to that of chloroform-narcosis your discovery is the greatest and most blessed in our Science. God reward you for it, and grant you a long and happy life."

Antisepsis in France and Elsewhere

In France there was published a book similar to that of Nussbaum. Appearing in 1876, it was entitled *Chirurgie Antiseptique*, and was the work of Just Lucas Championnière, who had visited Lister in Glasgow in order to learn the method. He wrote: "A few years ago Paris hospitals were reckoned among the very worst, even by some of their own surgeons. Now, surgery may be carried out in them as anywhere else."

It was the same in other Continental countries. Lister had his followers in Holland and Belgium, Switzerland and Italy, and it is not surprising that his tour of some of the surgical clinics of Europe in 1875 was a sort of triumphal march. Italy was first visited, mainly for purposes of recreation, then Vienna and Munich, where the professional part of the tour began. The students of Munich and Leipzig were particularly enthusiastic in their welcome to Professor and Mrs. Lister. The latter in her diary speaks of a dinner in Thiersch's house, and she records that Frau Thiersch, who was a daughter of Baron Liebig, "added a dash of Liebig's extract to the soup after they had taken their places."

The King of Saxony was among the audience at one of Lister's lectures, and an operation (removal of a loose body in the knee) was actually performed for the king's instruction.

The return home to Edinburgh was followed by fresh responsibilities. In his Address to students at the graduation ceremony Lister set a very high ideal. "In every question there is truth, whatever our notions may be . . . yet it is strange how often it seems to be disregarded. . . . When I was a little boy I used to imagine that prejudice was a thing peculiar to some individuals. But, alas! I have since learned that we are all under its influence, and that it is only a question of degree. But let us ever contend against it; and remembering that the glorious truth is always present, let us strive patiently and humbly to discover it."

In September, 1876, Lister visited America in order to attend the International Medical Congress at Philadelphia, the President of the Congress being Professor S. D. Gross. Professor and Mrs. Lister crossed the Atlantic in the *Scythia*, then the leading Cunarder, capable of making 15 knots under full steam and with all sail set. A cordial reception awaited them in Boston, New York, Philadelphia, and elsewhere; the whole tour being one of the most important of Lister's journeys as the apostle of antiseptics. He took a prominent part in the debates as Chairman of the Section of Surgery, and he did much to promote the acceptance of his method in America, although progress there was not so rapid as it had been on the Continent of Europe.

Lister's discourse on his antiseptic method was the great event of the Congress. "He spoke for three hours, during which he received the most unwavering attention. He first referred to the great trouble which attends a perfect use of the antiseptic method, and he acknowledged the wearying care attendant upon its use." But he believed that there was not a medical man who would not faithfully carry out a treatment which promised such help to the patient. "We may have good healing without antiseptic treatment, but we cannot secure the best results. Unless we use this method we cannot safely tie large arteries without deep-seated suppuration.

"When I read Pasteur's original paper I said to myself, 'Just as we may destroy lice on the head of a child who has pediculi, by poisonous applications which will not injure the scalp, so, I believe, we can use poisons on wounds to destroy bacteria without injuring the soft tissues of the patient.'"

Lister exhibited his carbolised gauze dressing, stating that carbolic acid was a penetrating and cleansing antiseptic. He said that he liked salicylic acid, but had found carbolic more volatile and searching. Nothing must touch the wound which had not been cleansed by 1 in 20 aqueous solution of carbolic acid. If, during an operation, an instrument be laid on the table, it should not be used again until it had been dipped into the carbolic acid lotion. Those who used the method did this instinctively. All operations and dressings were to be conducted under a cloud of spray, an antiseptic atmosphere. The dressing consisted in, first, protecting the wound by laying on it a piece of oil silk wet with carbolic lotion. Over this was placed the dressing of gauze treated with a mixture of carbolic acid one part to resin five parts. The whole was bound on by a roller bandage of gauze moistened in carbolic lotion.

At the close of his long speech Lister was heartily applauded. In the account of the proceedings in the *Boston Medical and Surgical Journal*, 21st September 1876, Lister was described as "a handsome man, with ruddy cheeks, side whiskers, and the shrewd canny eye of a Scotchman," an apt description, although he was no Scot. As a speaker he was stated to be "ready and fluent. Modesty is stamped on his every act and word, but he *does* believe in antiseptic surgery."

After the Congress the Listers paid a brief visit to San Francisco, and then returned by way of Chicago. It was a memorable tour, although, at the time, very few of those who met Lister and who heard his message realised what a profound significance it was destined to exercise upon the progress of surgery in America. Already there was arising the school of surgeons which has brought fame and credit to the art and science of surgery in that land of progress.

CHAPTER VII

THE MISSION TO LONDON

LISTER was now fifty years of age, and his position in the field of surgery was secure. The antiseptic principle had proved a startling success, not only in his own hands but also in those of his colleagues and contemporaries who had chosen to study the method carefully and to follow the technique closely.

Nevertheless there were many surgeons who remained unconvinced, either from a reluctance to break away from traditional practice or from a lack of appreciation of the "germ theory," the key which Pasteur had given to Lister in order that he might unlock the gate which led to this new world of surgery.

THE CONSERVATISM OF LONDON

On the Continent, and especially in Germany, Lister's discovery had been received and adopted with enthusiasm. At home, although the converts were perhaps less demonstrative, they formed a growing party, especially among the younger generation of surgeons. Throughout Britain there were men whose eyes had been opened to the wonderful possibilities of the new principle and who, by their teaching and practice, were steadily spreading the gospel of antiseptics. London, however, remained unconverted, apart from the few enthusiasts who had taken the trouble to visit Lister's clinic in order to study his methods.

The researches of Lister had excited the interest of pathologists, and, early in 1877, he was invited to address the Pathological Society of London. He welcomed such an opportunity, but before the address could be arranged there appeared an even greater opportunity, one which was to alter, once again, the trend of his career.

THE LONDON CHAIR ACCEPTED

One of the leading London surgeons, Sir William Fergusson, died on 10th February 1877. Fergusson had come from Edinburgh to London as a young man, and for thirty-seven years he had occupied, with great acceptance, the Chair of Surgery at King's College Hospital. A careful and brilliant surgeon, his services were in great demand, and patients of that time were often advised to go to Sir James Paget in order to have their complaints diagnosed, and then to Sir William Fergusson to have the offending part cut out. King's College was originally founded by members of the Church of England who disapproved of that unorthodox foundation, University College, or "the godless college" as it was flippantly called. University College was open to all comers, King's College was originally open only to those who were strict churchmen, although it soon became obvious that this rule could not be strictly enforced.

On the death of Fergusson it was generally supposed that he would be succeeded by John Wood, who had been associated with him in the teaching of surgery for some years. Some of those in authority, however, were of opinion that it might be a better plan to invite some more distinguished surgeon to fill the vacant chair. While the discussion was in progress an unofficial proposal was made to Lister regarding the vacancy, and Lister expressed his willingness to come to London provided certain conditions were fulfilled. Unfortunately news of these private negotiations leaked out, and the students of Edinburgh at once expressed their dismay at the prospect of losing their "highly beloved and greatly esteemed teacher." They presented to Lister a memorial with 700 signatures, begging him to remain, and assuring him of their continued loyalty. "Nowhere," they wrote, "would he find a more numerous and devoted band of followers." Replying, in his classroom, to this expression of goodwill by his students, Lister contrasted the clinical teaching of surgery in Edinburgh and in London. In London, he said, the magnificent opportunities were neglected and the teaching was, "when compared with our system here, a mere sham." Of course those words of Lister's were intended only for the ears of his students, and his distress must have been great when his remarks appeared in print in *The Times* on the following day. Next, a number of letters were written to *The Lancet*, accusing Lister of unjustly criticising his London colleagues. In a very temperate reply he expressed his sincere regret that certain expressions which he had employed should have been interpreted as casting a slur upon London surgeons. Nothing was further from his intentions. He had referred not to the teachers but to the system under which lectures were given without any demonstration of the patient such as had always characterised the clinical lectures at Edinburgh. The episode was most unfortunate, and for a time it seemed as though it would put an end to any invitation to Lister to come to London, especially when it was announced that Mr. John Wood had been appointed to succeed Sir William Fergusson. Nevertheless the matter was not allowed to rest there. An additional Chair of Clinical Surgery was created for Lister at King's College Hospital. On 18th June 1877 he was officially invited to occupy it. He accepted the invitation, and before the end of the year he had taken up his abode in London.

Additional light is thrown upon Lister's attitude to his London appointment by a letter which has been recently acquired by the Royal College of Surgeons of England, from which the author has been permitted to quote.

Writing to Dr. Murray, from 9 Charlotte Square, Edinburgh, on 8th March 1877, Lister states that the invitation to King's would "enable me to carry out the two objects which I should in reality have in view, *viz.*, the thorough working of the antiseptic system with a view to its diffusion in the metropolis and the introduction of a more efficient method of clinical surgical teaching than has hitherto prevailed in London. I should not care about the rank I held in the smallest degree, but I should consider it essential that I should be allowed to give a regular course of clinical lectures in the operating theatre twice a week, to be on the same footing as other college courses, and that I should not be required to deliver systematic lectures."

LISTER RETURNS TO LONDON

There was never any doubt in Lister's mind regarding the wisdom of making this new move. To many of his friends it seemed to be a retrograde step. It appeared unthinkable that Lister should leave Edinburgh, with the large numbers of eager students and such ample facilities for surgical experience as the Royal Infirmary provided, and go to one of the smaller medical schools of London, there to work in a hostile or apathetic atmosphere. Surely he might still direct, from Edinburgh, the spread of his antiseptic doctrine.

Lister, however, was not the man to choose the line of least resistance. He felt that he could best convince the surgeons of London by practising and teaching in their midst. To London, therefore, he must go, even if this involved personal sacrifice. Accordingly, in October, 1877, the Listers removed once more, and settled in No. 12 Park Crescent. The house was not in the consultants' quarter, partly because Lister did not wish to compete aggressively with other London surgeons, partly also because he would be close to Regent's Park, and to the amenity of garden walks such as he had enjoyed so much in Glasgow and Edinburgh. He never acquired a very large practice in London; nevertheless, patients were sent to him from all parts of the world, and such as required operation were accommodated in his private hospital or "nursing home" at 15 Fitzroy Square. There were only a few nursing homes in London then, as the majority of patients preferred to undergo operation in their own homes, an arrangement which was favoured by the family practitioner, who thus retained the case under his own control. It was essential to the success of Lister's method, however, that each dressing should be conducted under the same rigid precautions as the operation, and by accommodating his patients near him in the nursing home he was enabled to give them the close attention which his technique demanded.

LISTER'S ASSISTANTS IN HIS MISSION

It was for this reason, too, that Lister took with him from Edinburgh to London four skilled assistants on whom he could implicitly rely. Those four deserve full mention in any account of Lister's achievement, as they were responsible in no small measure for the success of the London campaign. Two were qualified house-surgeons, Watson Cheyne and John Stewart; the other two were student-dressers, William Dobie and James Altham. Fifty years later, Sir William Watson Cheyne, having meanwhile attained great eminence as a surgeon, recalled how he was chosen to accompany Lister to London. "Sleeping quietly in the house-surgeon's bedroom, I was awakened by someone shaking me, and to my astonishment I found it was Lister. He told me about his invitation to London, and he had come to ask if I would go with him and again act as his house-surgeon at King's College Hospital. Go with Lister to London! Of course I would go with him to London or anywhere else." Thus commenced the brilliant career of Watson Cheyne, who did so much to further the cause of antiseptic surgery. He was born in Fetlar, one of the Shetland Islands, and there he died in 1932, at the age of eighty.

The assistant house-surgeon, John Stewart, was a Canadian who had taken his degree in Edinburgh, and who subsequently became Professor of Surgery at Halifax, Nova Scotia, where he died in 1933, aged eighty-five. Like Watson Cheyne, Stewart was a tall, bearded man, and those two assistants of Lister must have contrasted strangely in physical appearance with their clean-shaven English colleagues.

William Henry Dobie was in his twenty-first year when he accompanied Lister to London as student-dresser. He spent a long and useful career as a general practitioner in Chester, and he outlived most of his contemporaries. He died at the age of ninety, in 1946.

James Altham, the other student-dresser and the remaining member of the group, was fated to die young, shortly after he had commenced practice in Penrith.

A CHILLY RECEPTION

Such was the band of supporters chosen by Lister to assist him in the eventful mission to London. They did not expect to be welcomed there, and indeed their reception was even colder than they anticipated. It was not that the surgical world of London was actively hostile; that would have indicated, at least, an interest in Lister's discovery. No such interest was shown, and the attitude was one of complete indifference, or, at best, of good-natured tolerance. As for the students, there was no need for them to hurry, as did the Edinburgh students, to secure a good seat in Lister's lecture theatre. Most of the benches were empty, and those who did come had merely strolled in out of curiosity. In Edinburgh, Lister's class frequently numbered 400 students; in London, some ten or twenty might turn up, but these gradually fell off. Ten years after his arrival Lister referred to his small classes at King's, after his crowded audiences in Edinburgh, as "a humiliating experience." The plain truth was that, as Lister's teaching was so far ahead of his time, few of his hearers realised its significance. Furthermore, however valuable the knowledge might be for the practice of surgery, it was of little service in examinations, especially as the examiners were surgeons of the old school. His lectures provided no "tips" for examinations. Lister had a contempt for the methods of the "coach" or the "grinder." Cramming had no place in his scheme of teaching; he wished his students to think for themselves, and he disdained all learning which did not include the understanding of first principles.

It is easy to imagine the feelings of dismay and disappointment which must have been aroused in Lister and his little group of assistants as they looked at those empty seats. In the graphic words of John Stewart, "We four unhappy men wandered about, and wondered why men did not open their eyes. We thought of the crowded hours of glorious work in Edinburgh and . . . we remembered the enthusiasm of an introductory lecture there, when the theatre would be filled with four hundred eager listeners, and our hearts were chilled by the listless air of the twelve or twenty students who lounged in to the lecture at King's."

But if students and London surgeons were apathetic over the revolution in surgery being wrought in their very midst, it was not so with foreigners, who soon after Lister's arrival in London poured into King's College Hospital from the ends of the earth.

Opposition of Nursing Staff

The attitude of London doctors and students was one of disinterested apathy for the most part. The nurses, on the other hand, adopted an open hostility towards the newcomers. They held fast to the cold, mechanical routine in which they had been drilled, and they appeared to be strangely lacking in kindly sympathy and sound common sense. This trait is well exemplified in the story of the patient who followed Lister from Edinburgh. He had left behind him a number of "chronic" cases whose progress had been slow, and great was his consternation when the Managers of Edinburgh Royal Infirmary decided to discharge seven of those patients. Accordingly he arranged that six of them, men and boys, should be treated in nursing homes at his expense, and that the seventh, a girl with a large psoas abscess, Lizzie Thomas by name, should come to King's College Hospital. She arrived on a cold October morning in one of the long wicker baskets which were used as stretchers in Edinburgh.* The sister-in-charge declined, however, to admit the patient until the secretary had arrived to complete the necessary forms. There lay the patient, in her basket, in the corridor, tired and cold after her night journey from Scotland, when John Stewart arrived on the scene. "I was too angry," he writes, "to see the comic side of the affair, but I said to the porter, an old Crimean soldier, 'Now, Vaughan, an old soldier like you can't stand and see a pretty girl lying on the stone-cold floor; give us a hand.' 'I will, sir, if it costs me my place,' he replied, and we carried Lizzie upstairs to the ward. One Sister attempted to bar the way, others asked if I was not ashamed of my scandalous conduct. I said I was not, but there would be a scandal shortly if they did not take my patient in, as otherwise we would put her to bed ourselves! The resistance gave way at this point, the girl was admitted, and in time she made a good recovery."

One of the main reasons for the opposition to Lister and his followers by the nursing staff was that he always insisted on carrying out his own dressings, and he did so with the same meticulous attention to detail which characterised his operations. Naturally enough the nursing staff could not understand the reason for this personal supervision, and they assumed that their ability was being called in question. After a time, however, they acquired the antiseptic outlook and became loyal supporters of the new professor.

> * You are carried in a basket,
>   Like a carcase from the shambles,
>   To the theatre, a cockpit
>   Where they stretch you on a table.—W. E. Henley.

THE MILK BACILLUS

The subject chosen by Lister for his introductory lecture at King's was *The Nature of Fermentation*. He began by referring to Pasteur's researches on the fermentation of grape juice, which led to the question, "Are all fermentations caused by micro-organisms?" Then he described his own experiments, performed with simple apparatus of his own design, to show how blood, if drawn directly from a vein into a flask which has been subjected to heat so as to kill all organisms, will remain for weeks without any putrefactive change. But if this lot of blood in the flask is touched with a morsel of putrefied blood, putrefaction will spread through the mass in a short time. Blood, therefore, had no inherent tendency to putrefy; it did so only when infected by organisms of putrefaction. Lister then proceeded to give an account of his experiments with milk, as milk was a more easy substance to study. Like blood, milk had no inherent tendency to ferment. If taken from the cow under strictly clean conditions it might remain sweet for many weeks. Various growths may appear in it, giving rise to curious colours—red, or blue, or orange—or it may become ropy and viscid so that it may be drawn into long threads, but it will not become sour unless one special organism, Bacterium lactis, is present. When present, this bacterium will outgrow all the others. How interested Lister would have been had he known that one of the organisms which he grew in milk, Penicillium, the source of Penicillin, would come to be used as one of the chief defences against many forms of bacterial infection. Lister further showed how, by counting the bacteria under the microscope, it was possible to dilute sour milk so that each drop of fluid would contain one bacterium, and with this fluid accurate experiments could be made. Indeed this method of obtaining a pure culture, discovered by Lister, remained the only method for some years. By those laborious experiments, involving many hours of close observation, Lister had shown that the fermentation of souring of milk was caused by one definite micro-organism which he had named Bacterium lactis. The audience gave the address a patient hearing, but they wondered what all this milk research had to do with surgery. A lecture of such striking originality, dealing with an obscure problem in bacteriology at a time when bacteria were hardly known, and delivered by a professor of surgery, was a bewildering phenomenon to the majority. Only a few realised the connection between the fermentation of milk and that chief blight of surgery, the putrefaction of wounds.

A Letter about Penicillium

Lister's keen interest in the new science of bacteriology and his careful study of the existing knowledge are well exemplified in a letter which he wrote to a former student, Dr. Albert Wilson of Leytonstone, who also had been attracted to the study of bacteria.

In 1946 there was presented to the University of Edinburgh a collection of twenty-two letters written by Professor Lister to Dr. Wilson between 1878 and 1888. The majority of the letters relate to various patients who had been sent to Lister for his opinion. The most interesting letter of the series, part of which is here reproduced in facsimile (Plates XVII and XVIII), is that in which Lister discusses the identity of various moulds and fungi and refers to the scanty literature on the subject which was available at that time. It is dated February, 1878, a few months after Lister's arrival in London to assume the Chair at King's College Hospital. The observations described in the letter show that Lister had a clear understanding of the significance of bacteria and of their relation to fungi, at a time when the "germ theory of disease" was by no means universally accepted.

12 Park Crescent,
Portland Place, W.
6th Feb. 1878.

My dear Wilson,

I am much interested by your experiments. I have never obtained milk under the spray, and in my recent experiments I avoided the use of carbolic acid or any other antiseptic for fear of confusing the minds of some of my brethren. But having learned by later experiments how extremely numerous the organisms are which enter milk when the spray is not used, your experiment with the spray is all the more interesting as confirming the trustworthiness of the spray.

Now as to your enquiries. The study of the fungi which you may meet with in such experiments cannot well be satisfactory without a study of fungology generally, and this, though extremely interesting, is both long and laborious. The best English book on the subject is Cooke's *Handbook of British Fungi*. But it is a systematic work intended for finding the names of plants by, and presupposes considerable knowledge of the subject. If you are a German scholar, I would advise you to read De Barry's *Morphologie und Physiologie der Pilze*, etc., published by Engelmann of Leipzig. Williams and Norgate of Frederick Street could procure it for you. It was from that book that I got my first knowledge of the subject, except that I had before read Berkeley's *Introduction to Cryptogamic Botany*, which, however, is certainly a pretty difficult book for a beginner. That book you would be able to get from the University Library, and for ought I know De Barry's also, although I doubt it. I will merely add that the commonest

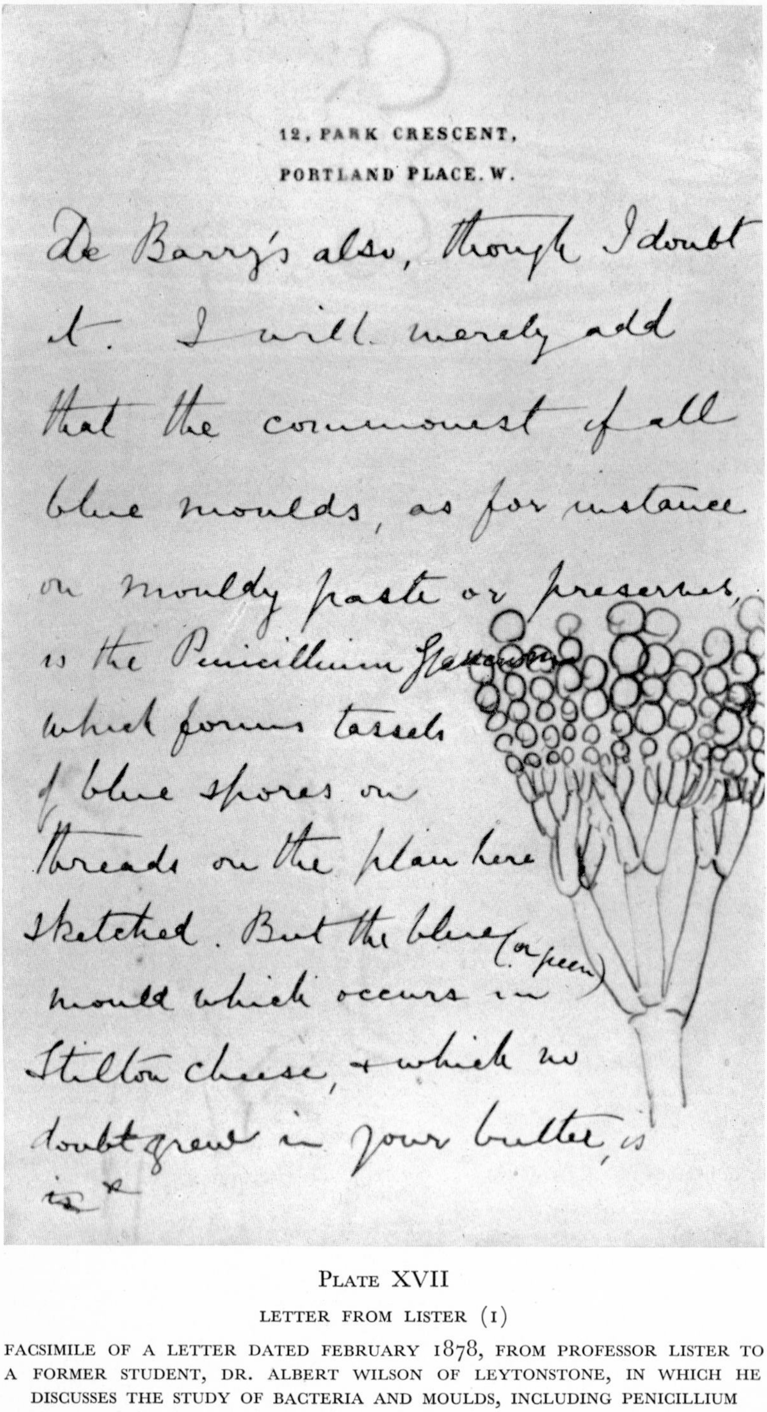

12, PARK CRESCENT,
PORTLAND PLACE. W.

De Barry's also, though I doubt
it. I will merely add
that the commonest of all
blue moulds, as for instance
on mouldy paste or preserves,
is the Penicillium glaucum
which forms tassels
of blue spores on
threads on the plan here
sketched. But the blue (or green)
mould which occurs in
Stilton cheese, + which no
doubt grew in your butter, is
is &

PLATE XVII

LETTER FROM LISTER (1)

FACSIMILE OF A LETTER DATED FEBRUARY 1878, FROM PROFESSOR LISTER TO
A FORMER STUDENT, DR. ALBERT WILSON OF LEYTONSTONE, IN WHICH HE
DISCUSSES THE STUDY OF BACTERIA AND MOULDS, INCLUDING PENICILLIUM

Between pages 96 and 97

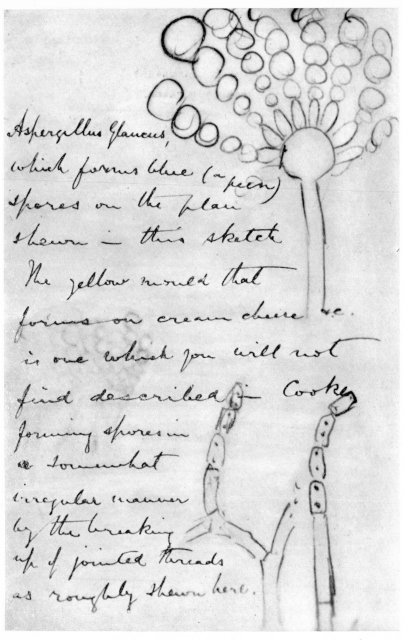

Aspergillus Glaucus,
which forms blue (a green)
spores on the plan
shewn — this sketch
The yellow mould that
forms on cream cheese &c.
is one which you will not
find described in Cooke
forming spores in
a somewhat
irregular manner
by the breaking
up of jointed threads
as roughly shewn here.

PLATE XVIII

LETTER FROM LISTER (2)

CONTINUATION OF PLATE XVII.   THE ENTIRE LETTER IS QUOTED ON PAGES 96 AND 97

Between pages 96 and 97

of all blue moulds, as for instance on mouldy paste or preserves, is the Penicillium Glaucum which forms tassels of blue spores or threads on the plan here sketched. But the blue (or green) mould which occurs in Stilton cheese, and which no doubt grew in your butter, is Aspergillus Glaucus, which forms blue (or green) spores on the plan shewn in this sketch. The yellow mould that forms on cream cheese, etc., is one which you will not find described in Cooke, forming spores in a somewhat irregular manner by the breaking up of jointed threads as roughly shewn here. This is no doubt what you have met with.

As to the bacteria, their name is legion. But the Bacterium Lactis appears, so far as I know, to be always a motionless bacterium. You will find this alluded to in my last publication on the subject, *viz.* an address to the Pathological Society of London, given in full in the *British Medical Journal* of Dec. 22nd, 1877. As to the way of telling if it is alive, that you cannot do at all of an individual unless you watch it in the process of multiplication if this be going on rapidly. But of course you can tell if they *have* multiplied by comparing their numbers at different times. As to the relation of bacteria to filamentous fungi, I cannot speak with anything like certainty.

You are quite right in your interpretation of the absence of rancidity in the butter that had been exposed to a very high temperature and afterwards exposed to air. The nutriment for bacteria was absent. I will end with a question. How did the butter-milk taste which you got by shaking up the pure milk in a pure bottle? Was it sour like common butter-milk?

Excuse haste,
Yours very truly,
JOSEPH LISTER.

Dr. Albert Wilson appears to have been one of the few persons who understood the significance of Lister's researches. The majority of Lister's contemporaries simply could not explain why any surgeon should concern himself with the fermentation of milk.

PATHOLOGISTS ACCEPT LISTER'S IDEAS

Lister, however, was determined to follow a logical sequence in his campaign for antisepsis. He must first convince his hearers of the nature of sepsis before he could teach them how to avoid and to fight it. Although the introductory lecture fell upon stony ground, the paper on the same theme, delivered to the Pathological Society a few weeks later, was more warmly received, because an audience of pathologists was more fully aware of the significance of micro-organisms in disease and of the importance of researches such as Lister had undertaken.

Lister also received a sympathetic welcome at the Harveian Society, when he discussed the influence of the nervous system upon the circulation of the blood in a paper *On the Influence of Position upon Local Circulation.* He showed that if the arm be held above the head it soon became pale and bloodless. If the limb was then tightly bandaged near the shoulder for ten minutes or so, it was found on removing the bandage that the limb became more red and engorged than before the experiment. Apparently the deprivation of blood acted as a stimulus to the vasomotor nerves.

This simple experiment, which Lister originally performed upon himself while waiting at a railway station, illustrates not only the activity of his mind in utilising every spare minute but also his versatility in exploring the realms of physics and physiology.

His address was an excellent means of commemorating the name of William Harvey who, like Lister, built up, step by step, all the evidence in favour of his discovery of the circulation of the blood. Those two great men, separated by more than two centuries, approached their problems in similar fashion.

It was perhaps natural that the surgeons of London preferred to judge the merit of Lister's method from its results. Patients interested them more than his lectures, and they failed to grasp the significance of bacterial infection. Indeed, Sir St. Clair Thomson has recalled that the surgeon in one of the largest teaching hospitals in London frequently raised a laugh by telling anyone who entered his operating-theatre to shut the door quickly, in case one of Mr. Lister's microbes should come in!

BOLD AND DIFFICULT OPERATIONS

Although those early days of the London pilgrimage were very depressing, signs of an awakening interest began to appear. One of the first to declare himself a convert was none other than John Wood, who invited Lister to assist him in a difficult operation for the removal of goitre. The antiseptic method was followed, and the spray was actually kept going all night in the patient's room, the disciple thinking, in this way, to improve upon the work of the master. The patient made a good recovery, the wound healing rapidly.

Still more spectacular was Lister's operation of uniting, by silver wire, the fragments of a broken knee-cap. Such a procedure filled surgeons with horror. To open a healthy knee-joint was in their view an unjustifiable risk. One of them even said that "when this poor fellow dies, someone ought to prosecute that man for malpractice."

Before this time the treatment of fractured patellas had been very unsatisfactory; the victim, if he recovered, remained a cripple for life.

98

Nevertheless Lister's patient made a steady recovery with a sound and useful limb, and a few years later Lister published a paper describing the successful results of "wiring," by open operation, cases of fractured patella and cases of fracture of the olecranon process (the bone which forms the point of the elbow). One of the patients had previously consulted eighteen surgeons.

In reading the paper at King's College he said that it must not be supposed that he came to extol his own skill. "How wise those gentlemen were in counselling against operative interference, provided they were not prepared to operate strictly antiseptically, I think we must all be agreed." The operation was perfectly simple and could be performed by any first-year student. The antiseptic precautions, however, were of the utmost importance. He continued: "Antiseptic treatment is not a very complicated business, either in theory or practice. You need not believe in the germ theory at all. All that you have to believe is that there are such things as putrefaction and other septic agencies, and that we have the means of preventing them. It is not a difficult thing to wash your hands in carbolic solution and to have your instruments in carbolic solution before you use them." Those and other simple directions Lister gave to his students for years after his arrival in London, and it was now clear that his doctrine was winning approval. "Gentlemen," he concluded, "I thank you most heartily for your cheers; for there was a time when such remarks might have met with a different reception."

Changes in Surgical Outlook

Thus did Lister inaugurate new and amazing developments in surgery, despite the fact that in 1874 his former "Chief," Sir John Erichsen, had said that surgery was rapidly approaching finality of perfection, and had predicted that "the abdomen, the chest, and the brain would be for ever shut from the intrusions of the wise and humane surgeon." Little did Erichsen think what miracles of healing were still to be accomplished in those very parts of the body. Knowing well what great advances would follow the general acceptance of his views, Lister now addressed himself with greater zeal than ever to his gospel of antiseptics. His clinics in Scotland had always attracted foreign surgeons, and many visited King's College Hospital. As has been remarked, his teaching was first accepted on the Continent. It was not surprising, therefore, that his appearance at the Sixth International Medical Congress, held at Amsterdam in 1879, was hailed with immense enthusiasm. When Lister rose to speak, the whole assembly stood up and cheered him long and loud, and after some minutes the President, Professor Donders, shook hands with him, and said, "Professor Lister, it is not only our admiration which we offer you, it is our gratitude, and that of the nations to which we belong."

LOUIS PASTEUR AND ROBERT KOCH

Four years later the Seventh Congress met in London, when Lister had the satisfaction of bringing together the two great pioneers of bacteriology, Pasteur and Koch. Pasteur, to whose work we have already alluded, had just completed a remarkable investigation into the cause of chicken cholera, and had discovered that by injecting into the birds a weakened form of the micro-organism he could protect them against the fatal disease. "I have no medical or surgical knowledge," he wrote in a letter to Lister in 1880, "but in spite of this I hope that my researches will be of some use. . . . My chief desire is to produce indisputable proof that microscopic organisms play a considerable part in some, and probably in all, infectious diseases." Pasteur's inoculation of fowls against disease marks the beginning of the preventive inoculation which now protects mankind against many different diseases.

Robert Koch, who gave a demonstration of his methods of cultivating and staining micro-organisms at the London Congress, was then in his thirty-eighth year, twenty years younger than Pasteur. He had commenced his important researches while he was a country practitioner in Germany, and now he was reaching the height of his fame. At the end of the lecture Pasteur, forgetting the recent war between their respective nations, grasped Koch's hand and exclaimed, "C'est un grand progrès, Monsieur."

It was natural that the chief event in the Surgical Section of the Congress should have been a paper by Lister, *On the Antiseptic Treatment of Wounds*. There were only one or two dissentient voices in the discussion which followed. Sir William Savory, a distinguished London surgeon of the older generation, had few supporters when he stated that he attributed the improved results to better nutrition and greater attention to hygiene. Nevertheless there were still surgeons who claimed that by simple clean linen results could be secured equal to those which followed the use of the antiseptic system. Chief among them were those who specialised in the operation of ovariotomy, mainly for the removal of ovarian cyst, a common form of abdominal tumour in women. It was one of the few operations on the abdomen to be undertaken at that time. Operations for appendicitis were unknown; the patients simply died of what was called "inflammation of the bowels." The ovariotomists were the pioneers of the surgery of the abdomen which was later to become a major specialty. Sir Spencer Wells of London, Mr. Lawson Tait of Birmingham, and Dr. Thomas Keith of Edinburgh were notable exponents in this operation. Spencer Wells was a well-known practitioner and his services were greatly in demand. For many years he lived at Golders Green, and he used to drive daily into London clad in a grey frock-coat and a white top hat, seated in his phaeton drawn by a splendid pair of horses. Wells performed his first successful ovariotomy in 1858, and by 1880 he had collected one thousand cases. At first the death rate was fairly high, about thirty-four per cent., but it steadily diminished until reduced to eleven per cent. During the early part of his career he attributed his success to the strict cleanliness upon which he insisted. Nevertheless, his results were even better after he adopted all the essential technique of Lister's system.

CLEANLINESS AND ANTISEPSIS

It is necessary to lay stress upon those facts, because even to this day there are those who allege that Spencer Wells, with his clean operating, was as successful as Lister with his antiseptic method. Both Wells and Lawson Tait, the latter a Birmingham surgeon of later date, were really following the Listerian principle by their rigorous measures of clean operating and their liberal use of soap and water. Tait boiled his instruments and his ligatures, thus employing heat as an antiseptic, in place of carbolic acid. There was, moreover, another reason why the ovariotomists should meet with success from mere washing as opposed to the use of chemical antiseptics. The peritoneum, the membrane which lines the abdominal cavity, has its own peculiar means of defence against infection. The abdominal cavity could be opened with much less risk than that involved in the opening of the cavity of the knee-joint. Lister knew this very well, as he had often discussed the problem with his friend, Dr. Thomas Keith, another former house-surgeon of Syme's, who had turned his attention to abdominal surgery, and had performed many operations of ovariotomy with conspicuous success. Keith also had assisted Sir J. Y. Simpson, and was one of the trio who, by self-experimentation, discovered the anæsthetic value of chloroform around Simpson's dining-table, on 4th November 1847. Writing in 1881, Lister tells us that, "several years ago, when Dr. Keith expressed to me an intention of performing ovariotomy antiseptically, I strongly dissuaded him from his purpose." Lister felt that antiseptics applied within the abdomen might cause needless irritation; nevertheless he "believed that the day would come when strict antiseptic treatment would prove invaluable in ovariotomy." He recognised that the cells and fluids of the body possessed in themselves antiseptic properties, and thus he foreshadowed the work of Metchnikoff, of the Pasteur Institute, who in 1884 showed how the "phagocytes," as he called them, devour the invading bacteria, and thus form Nature's powerful defence mechanism.

ASEPTIC SURGERY: BERGMANN AND NEUBER

It was not only in the field of abdominal surgery that good results were obtained by simple cleanliness. During the Franco-Prussian War, Ernst von Bergmann of Berlin had proved the value of what he called an "aseptic" dressing. The name was unfortunate as many so-called aseptic surgeons continued to use antiseptics. Moreover, those who had discarded chemicals relied upon the antiseptic value of heat. Asepsis and antisepsis are similar, not antagonistic. Although von Bergmann is regarded as the apostle of asepsis, he was really forestalled by Lawson Tait. Before either of them, however, was Lister, who visualised the possibility of relying upon heat instead of chemicals, but who never felt justified in doing so. Von Bergmann, while according to Lister full credit for his principle, proceeded to elaborate the method of rendering instruments and dressings free from micro-organisms by boiling or steaming. He developed the use of operating-theatres which could be rendered germ free, of metal furniture which could be thoroughly cleansed, and of steam sterilisation which could be applied to towels and gowns and dressings. Von Bergmann's assistant, Schimmelbusch, published in 1892 a little book on *The Aseptic Treatment of Wounds*, which had a wide popularity.

Another noteworthy pioneer of asepsis, although perhaps less famous than von Bergmann, was Gustav Neuber of Kiel, 1850-1932. Neuber had studied under Volkmann and Esmarch whose fame was world-wide, and had served in the Franco-Prussian War of 1870-71. From 1884 until 1932 he conducted a large private hospital at Kiel, planned and built expressly for the purpose of carrying out the aseptic technique which he had devised. There were five operating-theatres, so that "dirty" cases could be treated completely separate from "clean" cases, while the air of the theatres was sterilised by heat and by passing it through a cotton filter.

In the detailed account of his method which Gustav Neuber published in 1886, entitled *Die aseptische Wundbehandlung*, he laid stress upon five points:

(1) Disinfection of the skin of the patient by washing in a bath of mercuric chloride, then a clean gown to be worn, and, just before operation, the area of operation to be again disinfected with mercuric chloride.

(2) All members of operating team (surgeon and all assistants) to bathe with soap and water before the operation and to spray their skin with mercuric chloride solution. Next they put on caps and aprons, and donned rubber boots, all of which had been sterilised by heat. Hands and forearms were again washed immediately before the operation.

(3) All instruments and accessories to be sterilised by boiling, then placed in carbolic acid solution.

(4) Wounds to be irrigated with weak solution of mercuric chloride and a sterile dressing applied.

(5) Number of spectators to be limited, and all such visitors to undergo the same preparation as the operating team.

Under this system Neuber secured excellent results, and it became obvious that sterilisation by heat, where practicable, was superior to the use of strong antiseptics. Nevertheless further modifications of the technique were necessary for the success of Listerian surgery.

After the elimination of the spray and the "protective" there were many features of the antiseptic or aseptic technique to be discarded and altered before the surgical practitioner could be certain of good results.

IMPROVEMENTS IN TECHNIQUE

Although the marble pediment of the Surgical Clinic at Rome bears a carved representation of Lister operating, clad in a long white gown, it was not customary in Lister's day. Then, the surgeon did not wear a gown. Sometimes he would remove his coat and turn up his shirt sleeves, but more frequently he simply turned up the cuffs of his coat to prevent them from becoming soiled.

As the so-called aseptic technique developed, the wearing of gowns and caps by the surgeon as well as by his assistants and spectators became universal, although masks to cover the mouth and nose were not introduced until about 1906. Nowadays the ritual is imposed, as Moynihan remarks, not only upon the high priest but upon the congregation. "Every visitor," he continues, "takes a part, however remote, in the operation, and he is gowned, masked and wearing a cap, in all modern clinics." Catgut, for example, was a source of sepsis even when prepared according to Lister's directions. As early as 1882, William Stewart Halsted of Baltimore substituted silk for catgut in his practice, using a spool or bobbin which was held in the left hand of the operator during the act of ligating blood-vessels. He used black silk, as it was easier to see than white, and in 1886 Halsted also began using silk as an intestinal suture. Blood-vessels he ligated by transfixion with a needle and stitch before tying, and thus he eliminated the ligation of a mass of tissue, which he regarded as unnecessary and undesirable. He found that if fine silk was used thus, it very seldom became infected, although, of course, it remained unabsorbed. By 1913, catgut had been entirely replaced by silk at Johns Hopkins Hospital in Baltimore.

The Use of Rubber Gloves

Another noteworthy improvement introduced by Halsted was the use of rubber gloves. "In 1889 or 1890," he writes, "the nurse in charge of my operating-room complained that the solution of mercuric chloride produced a dermatitis of her hands and arms. As she was an unusually efficient woman, I gave the matter my consideration, and one day in New York requested the Goodyear Rubber Company to make as an experiment two pairs of thin rubber gloves with gauntlets. On trial they proved so satisfactory that additional gloves were ordered." The irritation of the skin of her hands and arms from which Halsted's nurse suffered is not surprising when one realises that in his clinic it was the practice, first to scrub the hands and arms with green soap, next to immerse them in strong solution of potassium permanganate which stained the skin deep purple, and finally to decolorise them by soaking them in hot oxalic acid solution. A few months later the assistant who passed the instruments also was provided with rubber gloves to wear at operations. At first the operator wore them only when exploratory incisions into joints were made.

Halsted's house-surgeon, Dr. Bloodgood, remarked that the assistants with their gloves seemed more workmanlike than the surgeon with bare hands, and he was the first to wear gloves as a routine practice when operating. By 1896, the wearing of gloves by all concerned in the operation had become a regular part of the technique at Johns Hopkins Hospital. Halsted himself said that "during the four or five years when as operator I wore gloves only occasionally, it is remarkable that we could have been so blind as not to have perceived the necessity for wearing them invariably." After the introduction of gloves the results of healing were improved, and the thin rubber covering interfered only very slightly with the sense of touch in the fingers of the wearer.

Almost ten years before Halsted, probably even in 1880, cotton gloves were worn by certain surgeons, in order to secure a firmer grip on the instruments rather than with the idea of preventing infection. One of the first to advocate the use of cotton gloves as part of the aseptic technique was Johann von Mikulicz-Radecki, 1850-1905, who was Professor of Surgery at Breslau. It appears certain, however, that the idea of employing rubber gloves emanated from the fertile brain of Halsted. The practice of wearing gloves spread rapidly, and very soon became universal in other countries as well as in America.

Those developments, however, were a natural sequel to Lister's discovery and a further development of the principle which he enunciated so clearly. Lister's attitude towards such new developments was expressed in the remark, "Asepsis in this imperfect world is not to be trusted, human carelessness and fallibility are common; it is safer to have an antiseptic." Lister knew very well that asepsis consisted merely in the use of heat instead of chemicals as the antiseptic agent, but he was fully aware, and indeed he preached incessantly, that this new method involved greater risk, and would continue to do so until it was clearly realised that æsthetic cleanliness and surgical cleanliness were two very different things.

Now let us return to watch him at work at King's College Hospital in 1883. An excellent idea of his personality and appearance is supplied by one who was his house-surgeon at that date, the eminent laryngologist Sir St. Clair Thomson. Lister, he tells us, "was nearly six feet in height, upright, well knit, compactly built, deep chested. His bearing was dignified and his manner always restrained, ever kindly and constantly considerate. His voice was soft and musical, but a trifling hesitation of speech had persisted from childhood. Although he was very conscious of it, it was transitory and never embarrassed his hearers. His hands were rough, as were those of all his dressers, from frequent immersion in carbolic lotion. He wore a black frock-coat and waistcoat of the Victorian type, an upright collar with turned down points, and a narrow black necktie, tied in a bow-knot. I never saw him wearing any other hat than the chimney-pot silk hat of the period. He was invariably courteous and polite, and he was very responsive, but had a natural dignity and restraint which encouraged no familiarity. His pupils were always addressed as 'Mr. ——'; I think it was well; it held our attention and made us behave with consideration and restraint in the presence of the poor and the suffering. Far from having that doubtful gift of being a 'good mixer,' I cannot imagine Lister being on easy or familiar terms with anyone who was not a colleague or a pupil, and he was generally serious and somewhat formal. He never scolded, only a slight sigh escaped him if an assistant defaulted, and any little correction required was made gently. I, myself, always felt that his soul 'was like a star and dwelt apart,' but I can only add that no teacher, no friend, no man I have ever known has left his impress on me as Lister has done."

The same observer has left on record his impression of Lady Lister, as she became in that year. "She not only loved and shielded him in every way, but entered intelligently into all his work and researches; helped him in his studies; worked in his laboratory; wrote his letters (even, it is said, imitating his handwriting, as there were no typewriters then), and when I arrived at his home in Park Crescent early in the morning to go with him to a private operation, I would find Mrs. Lister preparing and checking off his instruments spread out on the sofa."

The technique of an operation by Lister at that time was very simple. He never wore a white gown, and frequently did not even remove his coat, but simply rolled back his sleeves and turned up his coat collar to protect his starched collar from the cloud of carbolic spray in which he operated. Sometimes he would pin an ordinary towel round his neck. Lister had a curious tendency to perspire freely from the least extra exertion, and it was therefore his custom to have a nurse deputed to mop his forehead with a towel, at intervals. The skin of the patient and the hands of the operator and his assistants were treated with carbolic solution (one in twenty). Lister deprecated the use of soap and water as this removed the natural oil of the skin and thus lessened the penetration of the carbolic acid which has an affinity for grease. Towels soaked in the solution were placed around the wound. Instruments and sponges were steeped in the same fluid. Neither the operating-theatre nor its furnishings were specially adapted for the purpose. The rough wooden floor bore the marks of previous operations, the table was a plain deal board padded with leather, while gas or candles supplied artificial light when required. One advantage of so simple a method was that the student who saw it practised in hospital could reproduce it when he commenced practice and had occasion to operate in the homes of his patients. It has been alleged that he was a poor operator, but that is not true. He may have been slow; he had none of the dramatic dash and haste of the surgeon of previous times. But there was now no need for rapid operating. The introduction of anæsthetics allowed the surgeon to proceed with his work calmly, deliberately and carefully. On the occasion when rapid action was demanded, Lister showed that his dexterity was equal to that of other surgeons. As he told his students, "Anæsthetics have abolished the need for operative speed, they allow time for careful procedure," and he would often add a favourite maxim, "Success depends upon attention to detail."

This meticulous attention to detail which characterised all Lister's work is well illustrated in the following letter of instruction to a patient in the Channel Islands, and it shows also that Lister was at that time using iodoform along with his carbolised muslin gauze. The letter was kindly lent to the author by Professor Walter Mercer, of Edinburgh.

12 PARK CRESCENT,
7 *Dec.* 1886.

DEAR CAPTAIN PINEL,

I am sorry to learn that the scar has given way; but I hope that, with care, it will soon heal again.

I send by this post a piece of the prepared muslin for you to go on with, and also a piece of the prepared oiled silk which, as you may remember, is placed immediately upon the sore after dipping it in the lotion. Outside the oiled silk you put a few layers of the muslin overlapping the oiled silk well, though it need not be large. For the first few dressings I would advise you to dust a little iodoform over the sore with a camel's hair brush, merely a fine dusting of a small quantity. The Jersey chemist will supply you with the powdered iodoform, 2 drachms will be enough for you to get. You might as well dress the sore every day until you see that it has the appearance of healing round the edge, but after that you might allow two or three days' interval. I would advise you to keep the leg always up until healing is complete. Please let me know in due time how it is going on.

With kind regards to Mrs. Pinel,

I remain,

Yours very truly,

JOSEPH LISTER.

It was while he was at King's College Hospital that Lister was engaged in the search for a dressing which might be less irritating than carbolic acid. Numerous experiments were made. Thymol, eucalyptus and salicylic acid were each tried in turn, and discarded. Perchloride of mercury or corrosive sublimate appeared to answer well, mixed with horse serum to lessen its irritating quality. Gauze soaked in this fluid and dried, called sero-sublimate gauze, was used for a time but did not prove sufficiently absorbent. Lister next tried a double salt of bichloride of mercury and chloride of ammonium, the so-called sal alembroth. Gauze, containing this salt, and stained blue, remained in use for several years, but it proved too irritating for general adoption. Then Lister, good chemist as he was, discovered that a double cyanide of mercury and zinc, combined with a small quantity of an aniline dye, hydrochlorate of mauveine, would form an effective and non-irritant dressing if incorporated in gauze. Thus there came into use the double cyanide gauze which, when moistened with carbolic lotion, was a favourite dressing for many years. It was one of those improvements upon which Lister had spent infinite time and trouble in his own steady and painstaking manner.

Professor Lister occupied the Chair of Clinical Surgery at King's College for fifteen years. Although London had received him so coldly on his arrival, his reputation and prestige steadily increased from year to year. By his illuminating lectures and writings, by his practical demonstrations of his methods, and, above all, by his sincere and engaging personality, he had convinced the majority of his critics. Soon he had the satisfaction of witnessing the gradual acceptance of his antiseptic principle.

At last, thoughtful people came to recognise that the principle was more important than the technical detail. The technique might change, it might be called aseptic instead of antiseptic, but the principle remained fast and unaltered. Accordingly, as there was a rising tide in favour of Lister's methods, it was natural that he should become the recipient of the awards and distinctions due to one who had accomplished so much. In 1878, on the death of Mr. John Hilton, the surgeon whose lectures on *Rest and Pain* remain a classic, Professor Lister was appointed Surgeon-in-Ordinary to Her Majesty Queen Victoria, having been surgeon to the Queen in Scotland since his operation upon her in 1870. He became a baronet in 1883, an honour which in the opinion of many had been too long delayed, but one which was at that time seldom given to members of the medical profession. The Royal College of Surgeons wished to choose him as their President in 1888, but after careful consideration he declined this honour, as he felt that at his age he must reserve all his energy to the scientific work in which he was still so actively engaged. His position in London was now firmly established, his reputation was world-wide, but he did not relax his efforts. There was still much to be done, and the record of his remaining years shows how well he discharged his self-imposed task.

CHAPTER VIII

SUCCESS AND HONOUR

IT is not given to every pioneer to witness during his lifetime the full purport of his work. Many a man has passed from this life unhonoured and almost unknown, to be appreciated and revered in retrospect only after years have passed. How often do we speak of such a person as having been "in advance of his time." Lister, however, was one of those fortunate pioneers who, blessed with health and length of days, beheld the steady acceptance of his great discovery.

Innovations are not always popular, and for years the revolutionary changes in surgery introduced by Lister were often ill understood and were still more frequently misapplied. Surgeons were slow to grasp the new principle, and were unwilling to make those radical changes of their technique upon which the success of Listerian surgery depended. Nevertheless his mission to London, at first so unpromising, had at last proved successful, and within ten years the battle was won. During the earlier part of this period he continued his investigations upon micro-organisms, but as the infant science of bacteriology grew and developed, becoming an ever-widening field, he wisely concentrated his attention upon expounding afresh the principle of the prevention and cure of septic infections. Soon he was recognised as the leading surgeon and scientist of his time, and his services were in great demand as a lecturer and as a member of various commissions and committees.

THE PROBLEM OF HYDROPHOBIA (RABIES)

One of the most important was the Government Commission appointed in 1886, under the Presidency of Sir James Paget, to enquire into the efficacy of the treatment of hydrophobia, or rabies, which had been recently discovered by Pasteur. In this investigation Lister took an active interest. The following two letters, now in possession of Edinburgh University, illustrate Lister's deep interest in the problem of rabies.

12 PARK CRESCENT,
PORTLAND PLACE,
25 *Oct.* '97.

MY DEAR DR. WILSON,

Many thanks for your letter with the interesting statistics. There is a question

109

which it occurs to me to ask you. If I am not misinformed, the German Government have almost entirely got rid of rabies by universal compulsory muzzling of dogs. But although they only get *wolves* from over the Russian border, have they not foxes of their own?

Believe me,

Yours very truly,

LISTER.

1st *Nov.* 1897.

MY DEAR DR. WILSON,

I ought to have returned the enclosed before. I confess the writer seems to me much in the dark himself on the whole subject. If universal muzzling could be carried out, it would give the best chance; and it is undoubtedly a hard thing that shepherds should be made to muzzle their dogs and hounds should be exempt. But even if an order for universal muzzling could be brought about, I fear there would be terrible lukewarmness in carrying it out.

Very truly yours,

LISTER.

Readers of the delightful biography of Pasteur, by Vallery-Radot, will recollect how, after successful animal experiments, Pasteur treated successfully the Alsatian boy, Joseph Meister, who had been bitten by a mad dog; and then a second boy, Jupille, whose statue, representing him grappling with the dog which had attacked a party of children, may be seen at the Pasteur Institute. Although now unknown in this country, rabies was fairly common at that time, and it caused about forty deaths each year in England alone. Pasteur Institutes for the treatment of the disease had been founded in many countries, but it was still necessary to send to Paris any British patient suspected of having acquired hydrophobia from a dog bite.

The project which arose out of the Commission for the establishment of a British institute for the study and treatment not only of rabies but, like the original institute in Paris, of all infectious diseases, could not fail to enlist the sympathy and support of Lister, whose discovery had been inspired so largely by the work of Pasteur. This proposal, in which Lister played a leading part, was eventually carried out.

THE LISTER INSTITUTE FOUNDED

In 1891 the project took shape, and the British Institute of Preventive Medicine was founded, but the building, a large red block in Chelsea

Gardens overlooking the Thames, was not completed and opened until 1897. That year being the centenary of Edward Jenner's discovery of vaccination, a public appeal was made for funds, in order that the Institute might be more soundly endowed and established as a memorial, to be known henceforth as the Jenner Institute.

Various difficulties arose. The scheme aroused the indignation of anti-vaccinationists and anti-vivisectionists, and only a small sum was raised. In 1900, however, Lord Iveagh nobly rescued the Institute by his liberal gift of £250,000, so that the future was secure.

A further difficulty concerned the name, as there existed a commercial firm for the supply of calf lymph also known as the Jenner Institute. It was therefore decided to alter the name, to call it "The Lister Institute of Preventive Medicine," which name, assumed in 1903, still designates this institution in which much valuable work has been done and which has been the training ground and the sphere of labour of many a distinguished scientist. Although Lister, with his dislike of publicity, was at first unwilling that his name should be used, fortunately he relented, and the Institute remains as a fitting memorial of one who did so much for Preventive Medicine. Reference is made to the Jenner Institute in the following two letters written by Lister to Dr. Wilson about this time.

2 *Nov.* 1900.

My dear Dr. Wilson,

The Jenner Institute has nothing whatever to do with the vaccine lymph. The Local Government Board is in temporary occupation of rooms at the Institute, but the entire responsibility for the preparation of the lymph rests with the L.G.B.

In striking contradistinction with the experience you describe is that of Dr. Greenwood, the public vaccinator for Marylebone, who vaccinated my household a few days ago. He told me that in 5000 cases in which he had used the glycerinated lymph supplied by the Local Government Board not a single failure had occurred.

I heard the other day of a vaccinator meeting with many failures which seemed to be probably due to his way of purifying the patient's skin. He applied a solution of carbolic acid to it and then at once proceeded to vaccinate after merely washing off the acid with water in a sponge. Considering how powerful an attraction the epidermis has for carbolic acid, and how it penetrates into its substance, such a proceeding seems very likely to interfere with the development of the vaccine virus.

Very sincerely yours,

LISTER.

12 *Nov.* 1901.

MY DEAR DR. WILSON,

Your letter and its enclosure shew that what I thought possible is the case, *viz.* that the lymph which gave such unsatisfactory results was not provided by the Government but by the "Jenner Institute" in Battersea. It is to be hoped that the Government will before long see their way to providing vaccine in sufficient amount to allow private practitioners as well as public vaccinators to obtain a really trustworthy article. This of course would involve an immense increase of their laboratory establishment.

Yours very truly,

LISTER.

PROGRESS IN BACTERIOLOGY

This was only one of the many activities in which Lister engaged at that period. He was ever a keen supporter of international collaboration, and in the year 1890 he attended the International Medical Congress in Berlin, and read a paper on *The Present Position of Antiseptic Surgery*. In this address Lister spoke of the advances in bacteriology, made possible by Koch, when he discovered how organisms could be cultivated and separated by the use of solid media. He went on to tell that Elie Metchnikoff, at the Pasteur Institute, had explained how the white blood corpuscles act as "phagocytes," engulfing and devouring the bacteria with which they come in contact. The researches of Metchnikoff provided Lister with an answer to one of his problems. He had long recognised that living tissues in themselves exert a potent influence in checking the development of bacteria in a wound, and this mystery was now solved. The success of the abdominal surgeons like Spencer Wells and Lawson Tait, who trusted to cleanliness alone, was due in large measure to the germicidal activity of the blood. Here also, in Lister's view, was a further proof of the needlessness of the carbolic spray, which he had by this time abandoned. The tissues of the patient could be trusted to deal with such stray organisms as were conveyed to the wound by air. Some day it might be possible to dispense with drainage and with antiseptics in wound treatment, but Lister did not at that time feel that it was justifiable, and he concluded his address with a reference to the double cyanide of zinc and mercury which he had found so satisfactory as a dressing. The paper is interesting, as it shows how open-minded Lister was towards any advance which seemed to be of promise, and how readily he was prepared to alter his views and methods if the need to do so was apparent. One of Pasteur's favourite sayings was, that "In the field of observation, chance only

Plate XIX

THE MEETING OF LISTER AND PASTEUR AT THE SORBONNE, PARIS, IN 1892, ON THE OCCASION OF PASTEUR'S SEVENTIETH BIRTHDAY

Facing page 112

PLATE XX

BUST OF LORD LISTER, BY BROCK, IN THE ROYAL COLLEGE OF SURGEONS OF
ENGLAND.   A REPLICA, IN THE FORM OF A MEDALLION, IS IN WESTMINSTER ABBEY

Facing page 113

favours the mind that is prepared," that is, the mind receptive, though critical; open to conviction and free from bigotry. None exemplified this dictum more clearly than Lister.

The Berlin Congress was only one of the many meetings in which Lister took a leading part during the later years of his career as Professor at King's College. He joined in a noteworthy discussion on "Immunity," as President of the Section of Bacteriology at the International Congress of Hygiene in 1891, when representatives of the new science from many countries met to debate in London. It was a memorable occasion for all concerned in it.

Lister was now nearing the age of sixty-five, when he would be due to retire from his Chair and from his appointment as Surgeon to King's College Hospital. Actually, he was asked to retain office for an extra year, and he completed this arrangement in 1893.

THE PASTEUR CELEBRATION OF 1892

The year 1892 was marked by an important and memorable function, the celebration of Pasteur's seventieth birthday. This great master, though in feeble health as a result of an attack of cerebral hæmorrhage a few years previously, was still mentally alert, and was present at the Sorbonne, where many representatives from France and other countries were assembled to do him honour. Lister represented the Royal Societies of London and of Edinburgh. More than two thousand persons thronged the great theatre, and there was immense enthusiasm as Pasteur entered, leaning on the arm of President Carnot, the President of the French Republic (Plate XIX).

Speaking in French, Lister conveyed to Pasteur the homage and congratulations of the British nation. Pasteur, he said, had raised the veil which had covered infectious maladies for centuries, and had demonstrated their microbial nature. Thanks to his work—and this was a debt repeatedly acknowledged by Lister—surgery had been revolutionised and had been shorn of its terrors. Pasteur's researches on rabies were a striking example of his work, so original and so beneficial. It was amazing that one who was neither a medical man nor a biologist could solve a problem which had eluded many other investigators. He had evolved a wonderful method of anti-rabic inoculation against a terrible affliction. "You can well understand, Monsieur Pasteur," Lister concluded, "that Medicine and Surgery welcome this solemn occasion of doing you honour and of expressing their admiration."

At the close of his speech Lister ascended the platform and embraced Pasteur amid the loud and prolonged applause of the large audience. The scene is portrayed in a remarkable oil painting by M. Rixens. The meeting of the two men was a living representation of the brotherhood of Science in the service of humanity. There were addresses by other delegates, Pasteur, overcome by emotion, remained seated, with bowed head. His reply, which was read by his son, remains an inspiration to every one who engages in research. After referring to his early work on crystallography and fermentation, and to his use of the experimental method, he expressed the belief that Science and Peace would triumph over Ignorance and War, that nations would unite not to destroy but to build up, and that the future would belong to those who had done most for suffering humanity. "Thus I address you, my dear Lister, and all of you, distinguished representatives of Science, of Medicine and of Surgery."

DEATH OF LADY LISTER

In the following spring Sir Joseph and Lady Lister left London for a well-earned holiday in Italy. They had enjoyed many vacations together since that Continental wedding tour which had included a visit to German hospitals. In 1878 they had visited St. Ives, in Cornwall, where Lister, in a letter, speaks of the excellent sea-bathing. The year 1879 found them in Norway, where trout fishing claimed his attention, for though he was never a great sportsman he enjoyed fishing, and also skating when available. The holiday of 1880 was spent in the Pyrenees, as Lister had occasion to carry out, in Toulouse, some animal experimentation which was essential to his researches and which could not be done in England. The first of a series of annual visits to Spain was made in 1881, where, from Seville, Lister wrote to his brother, describing Murillo's last picture in a church there, unfinished, because the artist fell from the scaffolding and sustained a compound fracture of the leg, from which he died after amputation had been performed.

Among the holiday haunts favoured by the Listers were Switzerland and Tyrol, and there, as at other places at home and abroad, they were keenly interested in observing birds and in collecting flowers. Diaries were kept on some of those expeditions, and a page from one of them, reproduced in the biography by Sir Rickman Godlee, makes the reader wish that they may one day be published for the edification and delight of Lister's many admirers.

The last of those happy vacations, in 1893, was spent at Rapallo, on the

Italian Riviera. A few days after their arrival Lady Lister was engaged in pressing some flowers for their collection, when she complained of shivering. She had been stricken with pneumonia, often a serious disease in those southern climes, when it assumes a type known to the Italians as "pulmonite fulminante." Within four days she was dead, and Lister had lost the partner to whom he had owed so much during thirty-seven years of happy wedded life. Her interests had been completely merged in those of her husband, and she had been responsible in no small measure for his success. The inspiration and assistance which Agnes Lister had so constantly supplied were beyond praise. The Listers had no children, and to the inevitable sadness of his loss there was added a loneliness hard to bear. His sister-in-law, Miss Lucy Syme, now kept house for him, and did what she could to lessen his sorrow, but the house in Park Crescent was no longer the happy social centre which it had been during the lifetime of Lady Lister.

PUBLIC SERVICES

By a fortunate circumstance the position of Foreign Secretary to the Royal Society fell vacant that year, and Lister was appointed. No better choice could have been made. Ever keenly interested in science, Lister found in this work the fresh interest and stimulus which he sorely needed at the time, while his international reputation and his knowledge of languages made him a valuable asset to the Society. He had been made a Fellow of the Royal Society in 1860, at the age of thirty-three, years before he made his discovery—an unusual honour for one so young. He held the appointment of Foreign Secretary with great acceptance until, in 1895, he succeeded Lord Kelvin as President.

Although he had completed his career as a surgeon, he was still an exceedingly busy man and one of the leading public figures of his time. Another important Presidency was conferred on him in 1896, that of the British Association, which was held in Liverpool. His address on that occasion was one of the best he had delivered. It was entitled *The Interdependence of Science and the Healing Art*. He referred to the recent discovery (1895) of Roentgen rays, to Pasteur's victory over rabies, to the researches of Koch and of Metchnikoff, and to the success of the antiseptic system in surgery. The last-mentioned subject he introduced (to quote from *The Times* report) "with such modesty and reticence that none who were unacquainted with the subject would gather from his words the extent to which he has been a benefactor to mankind."

A further honour which came to him at this time was the presentation of his portrait by the Members and Fellows of the Royal College of Surgeons of England. This fine oil painting, the work of W. W. Ouless, a native of Jersey and a well-known portrait painter of his time, now hangs in the College (Frontispiece). It is believed to be the best and most characteristic likeness of the master surgeon. Another excellent portrait, by J. H. Lorimer, an Edinburgh artist, was subscribed for the most part by those connected with King's College. It was presented to Lister there by his old teacher Sir John Erichsen, and it now adorns the Library Hall of Edinburgh University. Those were the only two portraits painted during his lifetime. After his death a medallion, now in Westminster Abbey, and a bust, the property of the Royal College of Surgeons (Plate XX) were produced by the eminent sculptor Sir Thomas Brock, and are regarded as excellent likenesses.

FRIENDS AND ASSOCIATES

It would seem appropriate, at this point, to mention a few of Lister's friends and associates. In addition to his teachers, his students and assistants, and his surgical colleagues, there were others with whom he was closely linked by bonds of friendship. One of them was Sir William Turner who, born in Lancaster, had completed his medical course at St. Bartholomew's Hospital, London, and had arrived in Edinburgh to be Demonstrator of Anatomy, under Professor Goodsir, just a year after Lister had gone there to study the surgical methods of Professor Syme. The two young Englishmen, strangers in Edinburgh, met at Syme's hospitable house, and formed a friendship which lasted throughout their long lives. Turner succeeded Goodsir as Professor of Anatomy in 1867, while Lister succeeded Syme in the Chair of Clinical Surgery in 1869. Their ways separated when Lister removed to London, but Turner frequently saw him there. In 1903 Turner became Principal and Vice-Chancellor of Edinburgh University, which appointment he held until his death in 1916.

The following letter from Sir William Turner to The Very Reverend Dr. Wallace Williamson, written on the day of the Memorial Service to Lord Lister in St. Giles Cathedral, shows how highly Lister was esteemed by one of his oldest and closest friends.

6 ETON TERRACE,
EDINBURGH.
16*th February* 1912.

DEAR DR. WILLIAMSON,

I wish to thank you for the simple but very impressive service at St. Giles this morning, also for the eloquent appreciation of Lord Lister's work and character. I am, I think, his oldest friend in Edinburgh. We came to this city in 1854, being London students and graduates, he as House Surgeon to Professor Syme, I as Demonstrator of Anatomy to Professor Goodsir. We became acquainted with each other at that time, were mutually attracted to each other, and onwards to the last retained and strengthened our early friendship. You have formed a perfect estimate of Lord Lister's character, and in your address gave without any flattery a true appreciation of the man. His modesty, simplicity, absolute truthfulness, keenness of perception and extraordinary powers as an investigator were the most striking aspects of his nature. Notwithstanding the opposition which his views received in the early years, and the sneers and laughter which they not unfrequently evoked, he brushed on one side all adverse criticism. Deeply imbued with the strength of the scientific foundation of his theory, he worked it out in practice in minute detail, and established it as a truth which can never be shaken.

Kindly forgive this intrusion on your time, but I could not forbear a few lines to let you see how deeply I valued the address which you gave us.

Believe me,

Very faithfully yours,

Wm. Turner.

Lister and Turner had much in common. During the earlier years they discussed problems of physiology and anatomy, in which they had a mutual interest, while in later life both were keenly interested in University administration and in medical education. A letter from Lister to Turner, mentioning his intention of bequeathing to Edinburgh University the relics, which include the three Freedom Caskets, together with various Orders and medals, and which are still on view in the Library, is worth quoting:

12 Park Crescent,
Portland Place,
27 July 1907.

My dear Turner,

Since I wrote to you on the 28th I have decided that if the University should approve of my proposal made in that letter, I would add the gold casket containing the Freedom of the City of London to the things I offered to bequeath to the University of Edinburgh. My sympathies have never been with a merely examining body like the College of Surgeons, but with a teaching University, and above all with that of Edinburgh. It was thanks to its liberal and wise policy regarding the extra-academical school that I was induced to teach surgery when a very young man; and this led to my work on Inflammation which was the essential preliminary to that on the Antiseptic Principle. And I need hardly say how near my heart Edinburgh became during the professorship of Clinical Surgery.

117

Hence though at first it seemed natural that the casket containing the London Freedom should remain in London, I should much prefer that it should go to Edinburgh. This of course would be in case my proposal should be acceptable to the University Authorities, and I can quite understand may not be thought a suitable one.

Believe me,

Very sincerely yours,

Lister.

Another colleague and close friend whose career, geographically speaking, paralleled that of Lister, was Dr. James Matthews Duncan. When Lister first arrived in Edinburgh, Matthews Duncan was assistant to Sir James Young Simpson, and he and Thomas Keith had been the two associates with Simpson in the discovery, by self-experiment, of the anæsthetic properties of chloroform in 1847. When Simpson died in 1870, it was expected that Matthews Duncan would succeed him in the Chair of Midwifery, but that was not to be. Seven years later he accepted an appointment at St. Bartholomew's Hospital, and removed to London a few months after Lister. In London he conducted a large practice until his death in 1890. Under a somewhat brusque exterior he had a kindliness and nobility of character which endeared him to patients and friends alike, and Lister often relied upon the good judgment of this staunch colleague with whom he was associated in two capital cities.

A third lifelong friend was Sir William Roberts, a fellow student with Lister at University College, subsequently a physician at Manchester for thirty years, and finally, from 1889 to 1899, a London resident. He and Lister had many tastes in common. Both were keen field botanists and enjoyed fishing. Roberts took a lively interest in Lister's researches, and he was one of the first to insist upon the importance of physiology as a basis for the practice of medicine.

Those three were Lister's principal friends, but he had many others in the fields of science and literature, including Charles Darwin, who suggested to Lister the use of benzoic acid as an antiseptic; Lord Kelvin, whom Lister succeeded as President of the Royal Society, and Sir Michael Foster, the eminent physiologist, and historian of physiology.

Peerage, and Visit to Canada

In 1897, the year of celebration for Queen Victoria's "Sixty years a queen," Lister was created a peer in the New Year Honours. He was the first medical man to be thus honoured, and the well-merited distinction gave great satisfaction to all, but especially to the medical profession. Many congratulations reached him, but the gesture which brought him the most satisfaction was a banquet given by his old house-surgeons, clerks and dressers, one hundred and thirty of whom were able to attend, many of them distinguished men.

In the autumn of that year Lord Lister visited Canada, accompanied by his brother Arthur, to attend the British Association at Toronto and the British Medical Association at Montreal. It was on this occasion that Sir Michael Foster, the eminent physiologist who was his companion on the tour, made a happy public reference to Lister's association with the Quaker community. "In early life," he said, "Lord Lister belonged to a Society, the members of which called all men Friends, and now in turn, because of his inestimable beneficence and service to mankind, all men the world over call him Friend."

Freedom of Edinburgh: Huxley Lectures

In the summer of 1898 the Freedom of the City of Edinburgh was conferred upon Lord Lister and, at the same time, upon the distinguished Commander-in-Chief of the British Army, Lord Wolseley. On this occasion Lister made one of his happiest speeches, drawing an analogy between the work of the surgeon and that of the soldier, when referring to his fellow-burgess. In returning thanks for the honour, he said that while he esteemed it very highly, he regarded all worldly distinctions "as nothing in comparison with the hope that I may have been the means of reducing in some degree the sum of human misery."

A few months later Professor Virchow of Berlin came to London to deliver the Second Huxley Lecture, at which Lister presided. Rudolf Virchow was not only one of the greatest scientists of the time, he had won distinction in politics and was at one time the chief opponent of Bismarck in the Reichstag. It was owing largely to his efforts that the drainage system and water supply of Berlin were reconstructed on modern lines. He was noted as an anthropologist and had assisted Dr. Schliemann to explore the ruins of Troy. As a pathologist he was pre-eminent, because his great work on *Cellular Pathology* had disposed of obsolete and old-fashioned ideas. This energetic and versatile man was a friend and admirer of Lister, and he received a cordial welcome when at the age of seventy-seven he came to lecture in London. Along with Lister he proceeded to Liverpool, to take part in the opening of the Thompson Yates laboratories, where much excellent work has been carried out.

Two years later Lister himself delivered the Third Huxley Lecture, at Charing Cross Hospital, London. It was the last of his great public addresses, and one of the best. To-day it is well worth reading, as it gives a clear and excellent summary of his researches. He tells how, when he was house-surgeon to Erichsen, he found what he imagined to be "some kind of fungus" when he examined under the microscope a scraping from a case of hospital gangrene. Even at that early period he formed the idea that septic infection was "probably of parasitic nature." He referred to his investigation of the phenomena of inflammation in the transparent web of the frog's foot, his researches as to coagulation of the blood, and finally to his discovery of the source of infection of wounds. He recognised that further advances had been made which had led him to modify his original views. "But the principle that first guided me," he concluded, "still retains, I believe, its full value, and the endeavour to apply that principle so as to ensure the greatest safety with the least attendant disadvantage has been my chief life-work."

TUBERCULOSIS CONGRESS: ILLNESS OF KING EDWARD

The next great public function to engage Lister's attention was the Tuberculosis Congress, which met in London in 1901. This was the meeting at which Koch made the startling pronouncement that the tuberculosis of cattle, the bovine type of the disease, was not transmissible to man. Koch had discovered the bacillus of tuberculosis in 1882, and although his subsequent discovery of "tuberculin" had not supplied a cure for the disease, as had been originally hoped, he was the leading authority on the subject, and any new fact which he demonstrated was readily grasped. If Koch had been correct in his statement that the milk from tuberculous cows was harmless, then it would have become needless to test cattle and to slaughter infected animals. Koch's views regarding the difference between human and bovine tuberculosis, however, were regarded as unproved. Lister was in the chair at this meeting, and his summing up of Koch's paper revealed his shrewd insight into the problem. He agreed that Koch had appeared to have shown that human tuberculosis is rarely, if ever, transmitted to cattle. But of the converse view, that bovine tuberculosis cannot be communicated to men, there seemed to be no reliable evidence.

The strain of those many public engagements was considerable, and Lister spent the winter if 1901-2 in South Africa, where he found the rest and recreation which he had earned so well. Just after his return in the summer of 1902 he was summoned to attend a consultation regarding the health of King Edward VII. To the consternation and anxiety of the entire nation, it became necessary, on 25th June, to postpone the Coronation, which had been fixed for the following day. Lister shared with other eminent medical men the responsibility for this decision, and the same afternoon an operation for appendicitis was performed by Sir Frederick Treves. Appendicitis, formerly known as the iliac passion, or as perityphlitis, had been known for many years. It was described by Jean Fernel of Paris in 1554, and more clearly defined, and named appendicitis, by Reginald Fitz of Boston in 1886. Although the King was sixty years of age and the operation was not nearly so common as it is to-day, he made a speedy recovery, and was crowned on 9th August. The Coronation was made the occasion for the institution of a new Order, the Order of Merit, Lister being among the first twelve persons to whom it was awarded. At the same time he was admitted as a Member of the Privy Council, and on this occasion King Edward, well aware, from personal experience, of the triumphs of surgery and of his new Councillor's achievement, said: "Lord Lister, I know that if it had not been for you and your work I would not have been here to-day."

EIGHTIETH BIRTHDAY

In 1903, when he and Miss Syme were staying at Buxton, Lister had a serious illness from which he never fully recovered. The next few years were of necessity uneventful and were spent, for the most part, out of London, partly at Bath, but mainly at Buxton. Although he was no longer a prominent public figure in London, he was by no means forgotten, and as his eightieth birthday was approaching, it was decided by some of his friends that there could be no more fitting tribute of commemoration than by publishing the articles and addresses which he had written and delivered during his years of activity. Accordingly, *The Collected Papers of Joseph, Baron Lister* were published by the Clarendon Press in 1909. The Committee responsible for the publication included Lister's former house-surgeons, Sir Hector Cameron and Sir Watson Cheyne; his nephew and former assistant, Sir Rickman Godlee; also Dr. C. J. Martin and Dr. (later Sir) Dawson Williams, editor of the *British Medical Journal*. The delay was unfortunate, as also was the fact that the two large quarto volumes were too heavy and costly for everyday reference. Perhaps they may be reprinted one day in a handier form. The *Collected Papers* are still of great interest, as they form a connected sequence, and show how Lister's researches in physiology, in pathology and in bacteriology led steadily and naturally towards his discovery of the new principle which was henceforth to govern surgery. Lister never wrote a book, a fact which still further enhances the value of his papers thus assembled in book form.

The actual birthday, 5th April 1907, was an occasion of widespread rejoicing at home and abroad. Telegrams and flowers arrived steadily at Park Crescent throughout the day, and although Lister's health did not permit of many visitors, he received a deputation from the Royal College of Surgeons, and thanked them in person. British and foreign newspapers referred to his work in fitting terms, and joined in the congratulations.

The lonely and frail old man must have been strangely moved by the numerous tributes of that birthday, and he expressed his thoughts then in a letter to his brother: "What a change of opinion has taken place during the years in which I have been doing nothing."

FREEDOM OF CITIES

His last public appearance was two months later, when he drove to the Guildhall to receive the Freedom of the City of London. In his speech the City Chamberlain mentioned that Jenner had received a similar honour just over a century before, and he expressed the satisfaction of the City of London in placing that day "the coping stone to his (Lister's) monument of fame."

Early in the following year the Freedom of Glasgow was conferred upon Lister, thus completing the tribute of the three cities in which his work had been accomplished. The Freedom of Edinburgh had been conferred in 1898. He was unable to travel to Glasgow, and the honour was accepted on his behalf by Sir Hector Cameron, who had loyally championed his cause even in the days of adversity. Sir Hector said that there was a certain dramatic completeness in the fact that Glasgow, the city in which Lister had first introduced into practice the form of wound treatment which had renovated surgery, "should at the end of his career, make her contribution to that crown of honour which would in all time sit upon his brow."

THE LAST PHASE

That Lister's mind was still active at this time, despite his bodily weakness, is evident from his correspondence with various friends. In an unpublished letter to Professor Chiene of Edinburgh, dated 5th May 1908, and now in the Library of the Royal College of Surgeons of Edinburgh, he expressed a lurking suspicion that his methods were not always followed as closely as they should be. He wrote, "People attribute faults in their results to defects in the means used, when they are really the consequence of their not using earnest intelligent vigilance against septic contamination by themselves."

He was still interested in the catgut ligature, to which he had given so much time and thought, and his last publication was a short letter on the use of sulpho-chromic catgut, which was published in *The Lancet* and the *British Medical Journal* early in 1909. He had left London by that time, and had gone, with Miss Syme, to reside at the quiet little seaside town of Walmer, in Kent, overlooking the English Channel. He was able to enjoy short drives, and he still hoped he might have the strength to return to his London home. But that day never came. His weakness increased, and he passed from this life, very quietly, on 10th February 1912.

It was thought that he would be buried in Westminster Abbey, but he had left explicit instructions that his final resting place should be beside Lady Lister in West Hampstead Cemetery. The funeral there was simple and private, but a public service was held in the Abbey, attended by many dignitaries who came to pay their last respects.

When Lister's career thus ended, he left not only a noble example but a priceless and immortal heritage. Work like Lister's does not end with death, and one likes to think of him, as did his faithful friend Professor John Stewart of Halifax, by recalling Matthew Arnold's words:

> "O strong soul, by what shore
> Tarriest thou now? For that force,
> Surely, has not been left vain!
> Somewhere, surely, afar,
> In the sounding labour-house vast
> Of being, is practised that strength,
> Zealous, beneficent, firm."

INDEX